THE Storytime Craft Book

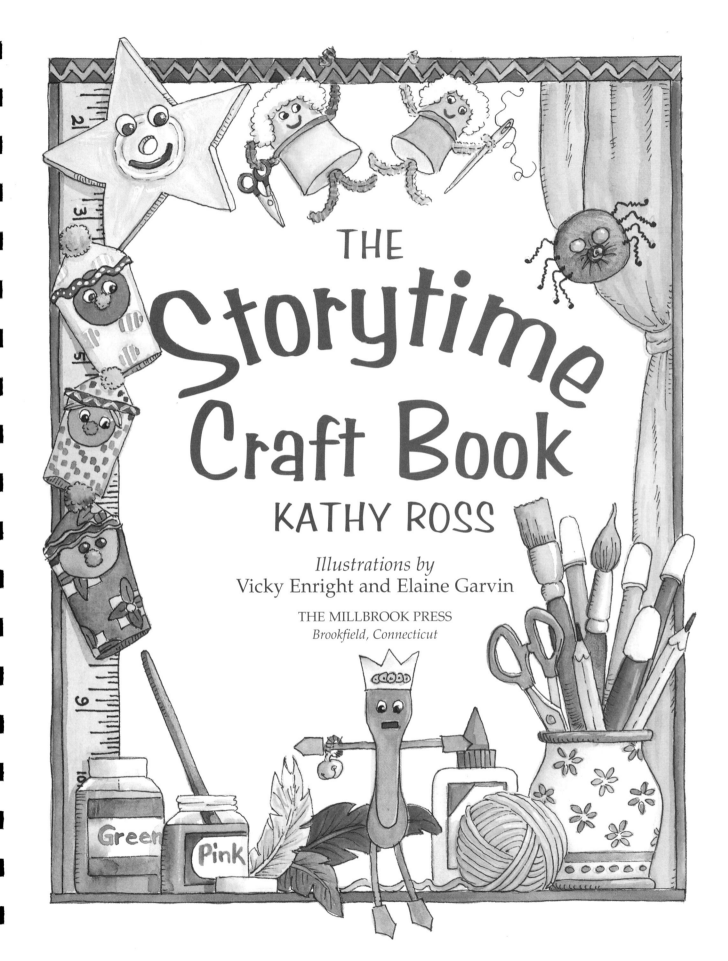

THE
Storytime
Craft Book

KATHY ROSS

Illustrations by
Vicky Enright and Elaine Garvin

THE MILLBROOK PRESS
Brookfield, Connecticut

Library of Congress Cataloging-in-Publication Data
Ross, Kathy (Katharine Reynolds), 1948-
Storytime crafts : hands-on projects based on favorite fairy tales, nursery rhymes,
stories, and songs / Kathy Ross ; iIllustrations by Vicki Enright and Elaine Garvin.
p. cm.
ISBN 0-7613-1843-7
1. Handicraft. 2. Fairy tales in art. 3. Nursery rhymes in art. I. Enright, Vicky. II.
Garvin, Elaine. III. Title.
TT160 .R714238 2003   745.5—dc21   2002008162

Published by:
The Millbrook Press, Inc.
2 Old New Milford Road
Brookfield, Connecticut 06804

Manufactured in China
1 3 5 4 2

Contents

Dear Parents and Teachers,

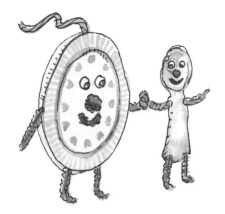

It is amazing how the songs and stories and rhymes that we learn as very young children imprint on our minds. Most grown-ups can still recite the exact words of "Jack and Jill" or "Rock-A-Bye Baby" many decades beyond childhood. Perhaps we remember because the learning experience itself was so positive, involving a good time and the total attention of a parent or caregiver.

I want children to be able to experience that positive sense of togetherness with parents in these busy times. So, using my years of classroom experience with preschoolers, I have developed a collection of hands-on projects, each of which enhances the experience of learning a song, a story, a rhyme, or a fairy tale.

The projects all require simple household or craft shop materials, and all have step-by-step illustrated instructions, so that even a pre-reading child can see how something is constructed. The crafts are designed to give the child a sense of accomplishment as well as to enhance the literary selections.

So get out your favorite nursery rhyme book or fairy tale collection or just hum a few verses of a song and have fun sharing your own happy memories with your child.

Kathy Ross

Nursery Rhymes

"Little Bo Peep has lost her sheep…"

Little Bo Peep Sleeve Puppet

Here is what you need:

an old long-sleeved man's shirt with button cuffs

construction paper in the skin tone of your choice

yarn for hair

white glue

ribbon and trims

ruler

markers

brown pipe cleaner

scissors

two wiggle eyes

artificial flowers

Here is what you do:

1 Cut one sleeve off the shirt about 12 inches (30 cm) from the cuff to use as the body for the puppet.

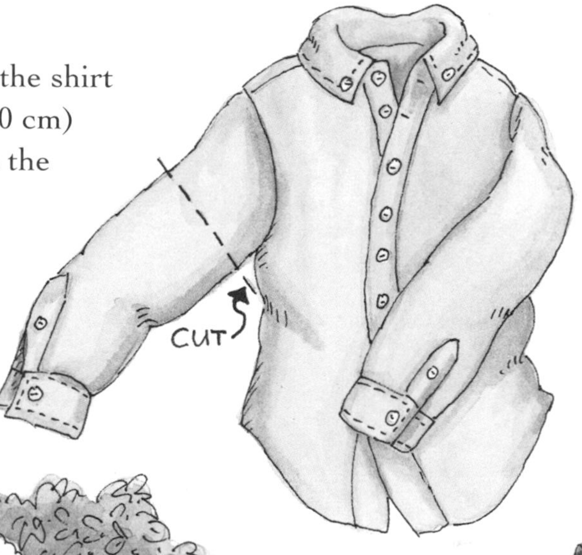

CUT

10

2 Cut a 6-inch (15-cm) circle of construction paper for the face. Push the center of the paper up through the sleeve to the end of the cuff to form a face, with the cuff of the sleeve surrounding the face to look like a bonnet. Glue the face in place.

GLUE SPACE BETWEEN CUFF AND PAPER

3 Use the markers to draw a mouth above the place where the cuff buttons. Draw a nose and rosy cheeks on the face. Glue on the two wiggle eyes. Cut some yarn bits and glue them around the face for hair.

4 Glue a ruffle of trim around the cuff bonnet. Glue a pretty bow under the chin for the tie on the bonnet.

5 Curve one end of the pipe cleaner to make Bo Peep's staff. Tie a bow on the staff and tuck in some artificial flowers.

6 Cut two hands for the puppet from construction paper. Glue the two hands on the front of the puppet with the tips touching. Glue a piece of trim on the wrist of each hand to look like the cuffs of the dress. Tuck the staff in behind the hands to look like the puppet is holding it.

7 Glue more trim around the bottom of the dress of the puppet.

8 Put the Bo Peep puppet over your hand and take her to find her lost sheep.

"This little piggy went 'wee, wee, wee, wee' all the way home."

Squealing Piggy

Here is what you need:

- two identical cups
- pink sock
- two-holed button
- pink embroidery thread
- pink pipe cleaner
- cellulose sponge
- ruler
- white glue
- water
- scissors
- two wiggle eyes

Here is what you do:

1 Poke two small holes in the bottom of one cup.

2 Cut a 2-foot (60-cm) length of the pink embroidery thread. Tie one end of the thread through the two holes in the cup so that the thread hangs down out of the cup.

THREAD

KNOT

SLOP SHOP MARKET

SALE

3 Cut the toe end from the pink sock, just in front of the heel. If you do not have a pink sock, use a white one, then paint the piggy pink.

CUT

4 Slip the sock over the second cup to cover it for the body of the pig. Fold the edge of the sock down inside the cup, then slip the second cup into the first cup to hold the sock in place.

FOLD SOCK INSIDE

5 Wrap a 3-inch (8-cm) piece of the pink pipe cleaner around your finger to curl it for a tail for the pig. Dip one end of the tail in the glue and slip it between the two cups to attach it to the pig.

GLUE

SLIP BETWEEN CUPS

6 Cut two triangle-shaped ears for the pig from the heel portion of the sock. Pleat the ears at the center of the bottom of the triangles and glue each ear to the bottom of the cup across from the tail.

7 Glue on the two wiggle eyes below the ears. Glue on the button below the eyes for a nose for the pig.

PULL DOWN WET SPONGE

8 To make the piggy squeal, moisten a small piece of the cellulose sponge with water and pull it down the string hanging from the bottom of the inner cup. Have fun experimenting with the squeals to find just the right noise for your piggy to make.

All mine

Where's Mine?

FEED ME!

Wee, wee, wee

"There was an old woman who lived in a shoe . . ."
Old Woman's Shoe Magnet

Here is what you need:

brown, yellow, and red construction paper scraps

black marker

scissors

brown fat marker cap

white glue

string

piece of sticky-back magnet

Here is what you do:

1. Fold a scrap of brown construction paper in half. Use the marker to draw a foot for the shoe. The marker cap will form the upper part of the old-fashioned shoe, which looks like a boot.

FOLD CUT

2 Cut out the foot part of the shoe through both pieces of paper so that you have two sides to the shoe.

3 Glue the back part of the paper shoe around the end of the marker cap, then glue the two sides of the paper shoe together.

GLUE TOGETHER

GLUE

WRAP

4 Cut a door and windows for the shoe from the yellow paper scraps. Add details with the marker. Glue the door and windows to one side of the shoe.

GLUE BOW TO BOOT

5 Fold a scrap of red paper in half and cut a tiny two-sided roof for the shoe. Glue the roof to the top of the shoe.

FOLD

6 Tie a piece of string into a bow. Glue the bow to the top of the shoe to look like a tied shoelace.

7 Put a piece of sticky-back magnet on the back of the shoe.

Would you like to live in a shoe?

SHINE SHOES

MILK CHEESE BREAD

A+

"Jack and Jill went up the hill . . ."
Jack and Jill Party Hat

Here is what you need:

old party hat

green poster paint
and a paintbrush

scissors

construction paper
scraps

white glue

green yarn

markers

tiny artificial
flowers

Here is what you do:

1 Paint the party hat green for the hill.

2 Cut the point off to create a small opening at the top of the hat.

CUT TIP OFF

GREEN

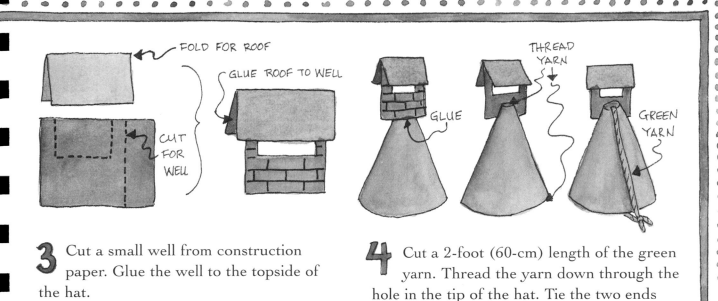

3 Cut a small well from construction paper. Glue the well to the topside of the hat.

4 Cut a 2-foot (60-cm) length of the green yarn. Thread the yarn down through the hole in the tip of the hat. Tie the two ends together leaving the loop of yarn loose enough to slide freely up and down the hat.

5 Fold a piece of construction paper in half. Use the markers to draw Jack and Jill about 2 inches (5 cm) tall and with their feet at the fold in the paper. Cut around the figures without cutting through the fold in the paper.

FOLD

6 Slip the back fold of the paper under the yarn loop on the hat, then glue the front and back sides together to attach the figures to the loop.

7 Glue the tiny artificial flowers on the hat hill to decorate it.

Move Jack and Jill up the hill, then quickly down again, by pulling on the yarn loop.

"Put her in a pumpkin shell,
and there he kept her very well."

Peter's Wife in a Pumpkin Shell

Pumpkin Bread

Here is what you need:

markers

two discarded compact discs (CDs)

orange and green construction paper

scissors

white glue

old glove

yarn bits for hair

two tiny wiggle eyes

masking tape

Here is what you do:

1 Trace around the CDs on the orange paper. Cut both orange circles out. Glue an orange circle over the printed side of one CD.

GLUE TOGETHER

CUT OUT

2 Cut through the hole in the center of the CD. Use the markers to draw a window around the hole in the CD. Add details to the orange paper to make it look like a pumpkin house.

3 Cut a stem for the pumpkin from the green paper and glue it to the top of the pumpkin.

4 Cut a finger from the old glove to make the wife.

5 Glue on yarn bits for hair and two wiggle eyes.

6 Use the markers to add a nose, mouth, and rosy cheeks.

BACK OF PUMPKIN TOP

TAPE

GLUE TO BOTTOM CD

7 Use masking tape to hinge the back of the top of the pumpkin to the second CD so that it will fold down behind the pumpkin.

8 Cover the inside surface of the second CD with the second orange circle.

9 Use masking tape to attach the finger puppet wife to the back of the pumpkin CD so that she is peeking out the window hole.

TAPE INSIDE PUPPET

To use the puppet, slip your middle finger into the finger puppet and support the pumpkin shell with your remaining fingers.

"Patty cake, patty cake, baker's man . . ."
Patty Cake Baby

Here is what you need:

fabric or net

pencil

thin ribbon

wooden craft bead with wide hole

clamp clothespin

scissors

markers

shoulder pad

white glue

yarn bits for hair

Here is what you do:

1 Cut a 6-inch (15-cm) circle of fabric for the dress for the baby. Dip the center of the fabric in glue and use the pencil to push the gluey fabric up into the hole in the bead.

BEAD

GLUE

FABRIC

TIP OF PENCIL

2 Use the markers to draw a face on the bead.

3 Glue yarn bits in the top of the bead for hair. Make a bow from the thin ribbon. Glue the bow to the hair of the baby.

4 Clamp the clothespin around the dress at the neck of the baby to look like arms.

5 Cut a hole in the center of the shoulder pad. Slide the ends of the clothespin through the hole so that it looks like the baby is lying in a little cradle bed.

Squeeze the ends of the clothespin behind the shoulder pad to make the baby "patty cake."

SQUEEZE

"Four-and-twenty blackbirds baked in a pie."

Four-and-Twenty Blackbird Pins

Here is what you need:

hole punch

paper fastener

scissors

two 6-inch (15-cm) paper bowls

black marker

seed beads

newspaper to work on

24 bird-shaped jigsaw puzzle pieces

white glue

yellow and black poster paint and a paintbrush

24 pin backs

aluminum foil

orange construction paper

modeling clay

Here is what you do:

1 Paint both sides of one bowl yellow for the top of the pie.

2 Cover the bottom of the second bowl with aluminum foil for the bottom of the pie.

3 Punch a hole in the edge of both bowls. Use the paper fastener to attach the top of the pie to the bottom.

HOLES

4 Use the marker to draw slits in the top of the pie.

PIE TOP

CUT LINES
BEADS FOR EYES

6 Give the round head of each bird a tiny triangle beak cut from the orange paper and two seed bead eyes, attaching them with glue.

Black

5 To make each blackbird, paint the plain side of each puzzle piece black.

7 Glue a pin back to the back of each bird.

8 Press clay over the bottom of the inside of the pie. Stand the 24 black-birds in the clay and close the pie.

This project is perfect for a class or large group to make. Each person can make a blackbird to display in the pie and later take home to wear.

23

"Little Boy Blue come blow your horn."

Horn-Blowing Boy Blue

Here is what you need:

newspaper

9-inch (23-cm) uncoated paper plate

poster paint and a paintbrush in the skin tone of your choice

blue and red large office sticker dots

yarn for hair

white glue

party horn

aluminum foil

pencil

construction paper in blue and in skin tone for face

scissors

Here is what you do:

1 Paint the back of the plate for the head of Little Boy Blue.

24

2 Stick on two blue dots for eyes and a red dot for the nose. Glue yarn at the top for hair. Poke a small hole in the plate where the mouth should be to insert the blower end of the party horn.

PUNCH HOLE WITH PENCIL

WRAP

SIDE VIEW

3 Cover the cardboard part of the horn with aluminum foil. Put the blower end of the horn through the hole in the plate so that it looks like the horn is in front of the mouth.

FOLD IN HALF TO GET 2 HANDS. THEN TURN 1 HAND FACE DOWN

FOLD IN HALF TO GET 2 CUFFS

4 Trace your hands on the skin-tone paper. Cut the hand shapes out.

5 Cut a cuff for each hand from the blue paper. Glue a cuff to the wrist of each hand.

GLUE

6 Glue the cuffs on each side of the mouth with the hands folded up on the horn to look like they are holding it.

GLUE HERE

To make Little Boy Blue sound his horn just blow on the horn from behind the face.

"Humpty Dumpty had a great fall."

Rōly-Pōly Humpty Dumpty

Here is what you need:

clear plastic wrap

yellow clay or modeling compound

yarn

colored hole reinforcements

plastic egg that opens

scissors

large-size office sticker dots

GLUE white glue

thin ribbon

Here is what you do:

1 Roll a 1-inch (2.5-cm) ball of yellow clay for the yolk of the egg. Put it inside the wider bottom part of the egg. Place a piece of crumpled plastic wrap over it for the egg white. Close the egg. The egg should now stand on end and wobble because of the weight of the ball of clay in the egg.

2 Glue yarn bits on top of the egg for hair.

3 Add a face to the egg using the colored reinforcements and office dots.

4 Tie a piece of the ribbon into a bow. Glue the bow on the egg below the mouth.

Set Humpty Dumpty on a box wall and loosen the two parts of the egg so it will "break" open when it falls off the wall.

LOOSEN THE TWO PARTS

SHOE BOX

"Old Mother Hubbard went to
the cupboard to get her poor dog a bone."

Old Mother Hubbard's Dog

Here is what you need:

white glue

black film canister

two wiggle eyes

old stretchy glove

brown construction paper scrap

small brown pom-pom

brown and red pipe cleaners

scissors

fiberfill

Here is what you do:

1 The film canister will become the head for the dog, with the bottom of the canister his snout. Cut two ears from the brown paper. Glue an ear on each side of the canister.

CANISTER BOTTOM

2 Glue the two wiggle eyes on the canister in front of the ears. Glue the pom-pom on the bottom of the canister for the nose.

FIBER FILL

3 Push enough fiberfill into the canister to make it fit snuggly on your finger.

4 Put the glove on your hand for the body of the dog. Cover the middle finger of the glove with glue, then position the canister with the eyes up and slide it onto your finger.

TAIL

POKE THROUGH GLOVE NEAR WRISTBAND. THEN TWIST OVER TO SECURE

5 Stick a piece of brown pipe cleaner through the glove at the opposite end from the head. Twist the end of the pipe cleaner around itself to secure it to the glove for a tail.

6 Wrap a piece of red pipe cleaner loosely around the neck of the dog and wrap the two ends together to make a collar.

ADD COLLAR

This dog puppet is so cute that if you make him sit up and beg, someone is sure to give him a bone.

"Hickity, Pickity, my black hen,
she lays eggs for gentlemen."

Egg-Laying Black Hen

Here is what you need:

white glue

black craft feathers

old black stretchy glove

yellow and red rickrack trim

small plastic egg

two wiggle eyes

scissors

Here is what you do:

1 The thumb of the glove will be the head of the hen. Glue a wiggle eye on each side of the thumb.

2 Cut a point of yellow rickrack and glue it on the side of the thumb for the beak.

ATTACH ON THUMB TOP

ATTACH ON THUMB EDGE

SIDE #1   SIDE #2

3 Cut a strip of red rickrack to glue across the top of the thumb for the comb.

4 Glue the black craft feathers on both sides of the fingers.

5 Slip the plastic egg up inside the glove.

When you want the black hen to lay an egg, make lots of cackling sounds and gently squeeze the hen to work the egg out of the glove.

"And the dish ran away with the spoon."

Runaway Dish and Spoon Puppet

Here is what you need:

three 9-inch (23-cm) uncoated paper plates

newspaper to work on

poster paint and a paintbrush

two large and two small wiggle eyes

one large and one small pom-pom

pipe cleaners

yarn

ruler

scissors

white glue

plastic spoon

aluminum foil

cardboard paper towel tube

hole punch

Here is what you do:

1 Paint the eating side of one paper plate to look like a dinner plate.

31

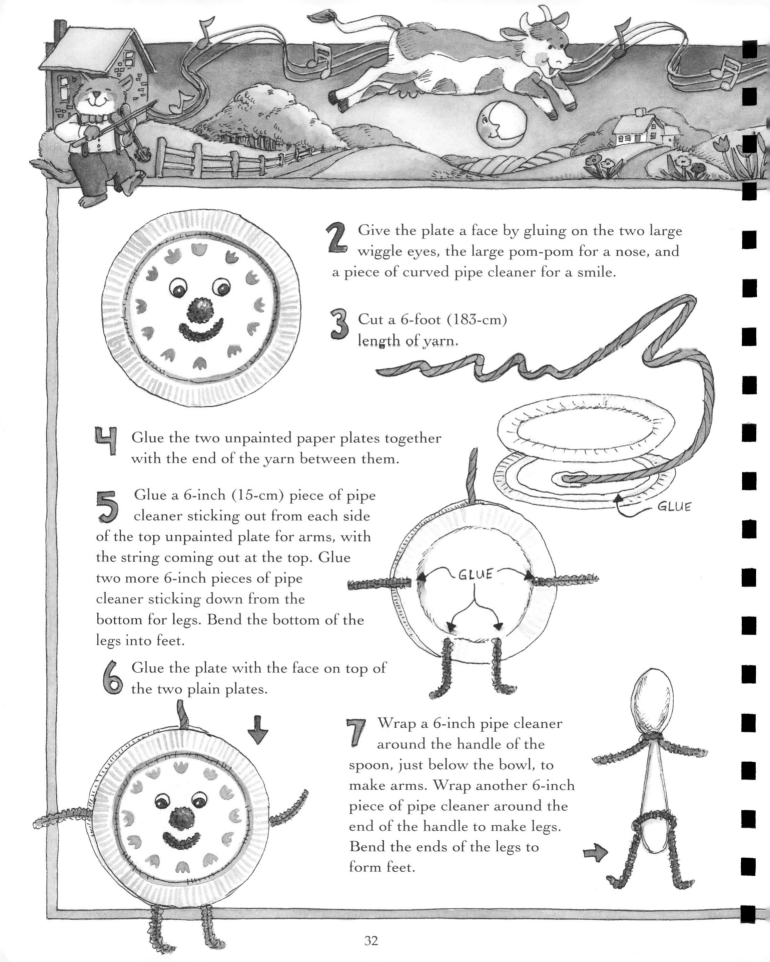

2 Give the plate a face by gluing on the two large wiggle eyes, the large pom-pom for a nose, and a piece of curved pipe cleaner for a smile.

3 Cut a 6-foot (183-cm) length of yarn.

4 Glue the two unpainted paper plates together with the end of the yarn between them.

GLUE

5 Glue a 6-inch (15-cm) piece of pipe cleaner sticking out from each side of the top unpainted plate for arms, with the string coming out at the top. Glue two more 6-inch pieces of pipe cleaner sticking down from the bottom for legs. Bend the bottom of the legs into feet.

GLUE

6 Glue the plate with the face on top of the two plain plates.

7 Wrap a 6-inch pipe cleaner around the handle of the spoon, just below the bowl, to make arms. Wrap another 6-inch piece of pipe cleaner around the end of the handle to make legs. Bend the ends of the legs to form feet.

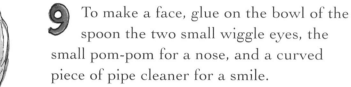

8 Cover the plastic spoon with aluminum foil, working around the arms and legs.

9 To make a face, glue on the bowl of the spoon the two small wiggle eyes, the small pom-pom for a nose, and a curved piece of pipe cleaner for a smile.

10 Join the dish and the spoon by wrapping their two pipe cleaner arms together at the ends to look like they are holding hands.

11 Punch a hole in the top and bottom edge of each side of the cardboard tube.

12 Thread the yarn up through both holes on one side of the tube and down through the other two holes on the opposite side. Tie the end of the yarn around the waist of the spoon, with the puppets at a height that is easy for you to work.

13 Work the puppets by pulling on the yarn across the top of the tube.

HOLES

THREAD YARN UP

""Hickory Dickory, Dock.
The mouse ran up the clock."

Clock and Mouse Costume

Here is what you need:

white glue

full-size brown
grocery bag

old mitten

two wiggle eyes

scissors

yarn

old calendar
page

felt scrap

ruler

pom-pom

Here is what you do:

1 Cut a 9-inch (23-cm) circle out of
the top part of the side of the bag
for the face of the clock.

> HINT: USE A PAPER PLATE OR
> DISH TO HELP MAKE THE
> CIRCLE

2 Cut the numbers 1 through 12
from the page of the calendar. Glue
the numbers around the hole
to look like the numbers
on a clock.

3 The mitten will become the mouse with the thumb forming the tail. Glue the two wiggle eyes on the end of the mitten on the thumb side.

YARN

4 Cut two 3-inch (8-cm) pieces of yarn. Glue the yarn to the top of the mitten, below the eyes, for the whiskers. Glue the pom-pom over the center of the whiskers for a nose.

5 Cut two 2-inch (5-cm) circles from the felt for the ears. Glue an ear on each side of the mitten.

TIC TOC TIC TOC

11 12 1
10 2
9 3
8 4
7 6 5

Put the bag clock on over your head so that your face becomes the face of the clock. Put the mitten mouse on your hand and run him up the clock and down again.

"Along came a spider and sat down beside her, and frightened Miss Muffet away."

Spider Car Antenna Friend

Here is what you need:

2-inch (5-cm) Styrofoam ball

discarded black panty hose

two thumbtacks

white glue

scissors

ballpoint pen

8 hairpins

Here is what you do:

1 Cut a leg off the panty hose.

CUT

36

2 Slip the Styrofoam ball into the leg of the panty hose. Knot the panty hose at each end of the ball to cover the ball. Trim off the excess panty hose.

3 Put the two thumbtacks into the ball above the knot at one end to make eyes for the spider.

4 Spread each hairpin to make the legs. Dip one end of each hairpin in the glue, then stick four hairpin legs into each side of the spider.

CUT

CUT

KNOT

SPREAD

BEND FOR FOOT

GLUE

5 Bend the end of each leg out to form a foot.

6 Use the ballpoint pen to poke a small hole through the bottom of the spider to make it easier to slip the spider on the antenna of a car.

Remember to ask a grown-up to take the spider off the antenna before going through the car wash. Just like the itsy-bitsy spider, this one, too, could get washed away!

HOLE

"The Knave of Hearts, he stole those tarts, and took them clean away."

Tart-Stealing Knave

Here is what you need:

white glue

four red craft beads

paper clip

old deck of cards

masking tape

two craft sticks

aluminum foil

sticky-back magnet

Here is what you do:

1 Wrap the bottom and sides of each of the red beads in a tiny piece of aluminum foil so that they look like berry tarts in tiny tins.

2 Shape a folded piece of foil into a tray to hold the tarts. Glue the tarts on the tray.

GLUE

3 Glue one end of the paper clip to the bottom of the tray so that it sticks out on one side. Secure the glued paper clip with a piece of masking tape.

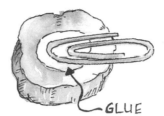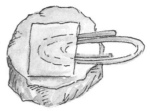

GLUE

GLUE TOGETHER →

4 To make the queen puppet, glue a queen of hearts card to a second card with the end of a craft stick between them so that it sticks out from the bottom of the card for a holder.

5 Make the knave puppet in the same way using the knave of hearts card.

6 Set the queen and knave puppets down next to each other. Put a square of sticky-back magnet on the center of the inside edge of the card. Put a 2-inch (5-cm) strip of sticky-back magnet sticking out like an arm from the inside edge of the knave.

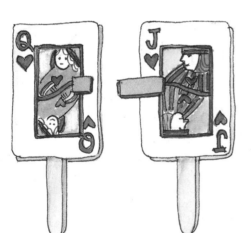

To use the puppets, stick the tarts on the magnet on the queen with the paper clip sticking out the side. Have the knave of hearts puppet sneak up and grab the tarts by the paper clip with the magnetic arm, so that the tarts stick to the arm. Then he should run away!

"Old King Cole was a merry old soul."

Old King Cole's Crown

Here is what you need:

colored plastic tape

scissors

white glue

pony craft beads

8-inch (20-cm) aluminum pie tin

Here is what you do:

1 Cut across the center of the pie tin without cutting the edges. Cut across the tin again to make four equal sections. Cut each section in half, but do not cut through the rim of the tin.

CENTER CUT

CUT 4 PARTS

CUT 8 PARTS

LIFT UP

2 Turn the tin upside down. Fold up all the sections of the cut tin to form to points of the crown.

FOLD TAPE OVER EDGE

3 Most pie tins are quite flimsy now, but if you have a sturdy pie tin that seems to have sharp edges, cover the cut edges with colored plastic tape.

4 Glue a pony bead on each point.

Put on the crown and call for your pipe, your bowl, and your fiddlers three.

"With silver bells and cockleshells
and pretty maids all in a row."

Mistress Mary's Bouquet

Here is what you need:

green pipe cleaners

construction paper scraps

photographs or greeting cards with girls' faces

ribbon

large plastic cap from laundry bottle

scissors

jingle bells

white glue

shells

artificial flowers

Here is what you do:

1 To make each "pretty maid" flower cut two 3-inch (8-cm) circles from construction paper. Cut 1-inch (2.5-cm) slits around the outside of the circles. Fold the cut sections of the two circles forward to look like the petals of a flower.

FOLD PETALS FORWARD

CUT LINES

SIDE VIEW

Cockle Shells

Silver Bells

Daisies

2 Turn the circles so that the petals are not exactly lined up to give the flower dimension. Glue the two circles together at the center with the end of a 6-inch (15-cm) pipe cleaner between them to hang down for the stem. Glue a head shot of you or a friend cut from a photograph, or heads cut from greeting cards, in the center of each flower.

TURN

BOTTOM FLOWER

GLUE AREA

TOP FLOWER

3 String some jingle bells along a 6-inch (15-cm) pipe cleaner to make "silver bells."

WRAP AROUND

GLUE

4 To make cockleshells glue a seashell to one end of a 6-inch (15-cm) pipe cleaner.

BACK VIEW

FRONT VIEW

5 Tie a ribbon around the cap to make a container for the flowers.

6 Arrange the flowers with some artificial flowers in the plastic cap.

This bouquet makes an extra-special gift when it contains a photograph of you or your mom or grandma.

To: Grandma

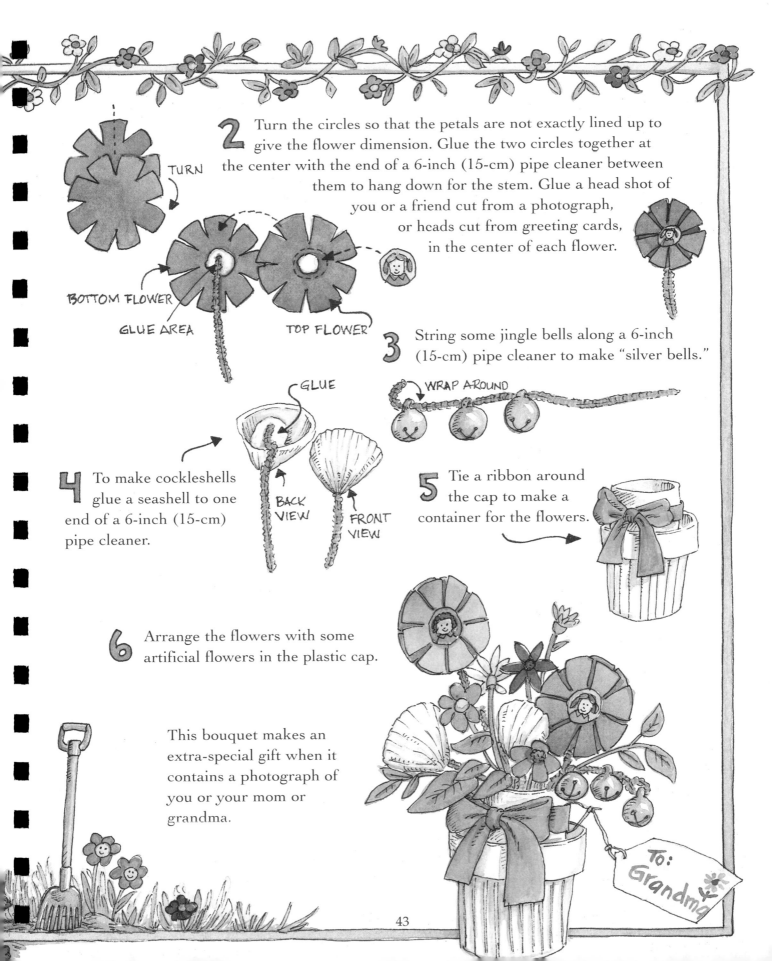

"Three little kittens lost their mittens and they began to cry."

Crying Kitten Soap Dispenser

Here is what you need:

- Styrofoam meat tray
- two pump bottles of clear soap
- ruler
- jingle bell
- scissors
- pipe cleaner
- two rubber bands
- black permanent marker
- flexi-straw
- black trash bag

Here is what you do:

1 Hold the two soap pumps together with a rubber band with the spouts pointing sideways.

2 Wrap both bottles in a large piece of trash bag, with the spouts poked through, and held in place under the spouts with a rubber band.

TUCK UNDER

POKE SPOUTS THROUGH PLASTIC & WRAP OVER TO BACK. TUCK INTO RUBBER BAND

3 Cut a 4-inch (10-cm) circle from the Styrofoam tray for the head of the kitten. Cut two triangle ears from the top of the head.

CUT FOR EARS

4 Press the two spouts through the back of the head at about where the bottom of eyes will be on the face. Take the head off again.

SPOUTS

5 Use the marker to give the kitten a face.

HOLES

6 Thread the jingle bell on a 6-inch (15-cm) pipe cleaner and wrap the two ends together to make a collar for the kitten. Hang the collar over the two spouts so that the jingle bell hangs down in front of the spouts.

WRAP ENDS

7 Put the head back on by poking the two spouts through the two holes in the face.

8 Poke the bottom end of the flexi-straw through the back of the trash-bag covering, between the two bottles of soap, so that the bent end of the straw sticks up to form a tail.

Every time you wash your hands the kitten will "cry." Meeeeow, meeeeow!

"He stuck in his thumb and pulled out a plum."

Pull Out a Plum From the Pie

PLUM

Here is what you need:

newspaper

two 9-inch (23-cm) uncoated paper plates

yellow poster paint and a paintbrush

ruler

scissors

pencil

construction paper in purple, red, green, and the skin tone of your choice

white glue

paper fastener

trim

Here is what you do:

1 Paint the bottom (not the eating side) of one paper plate yellow for the top piecrust.

YELLOW

PLATE BOTTOM

PING PONG

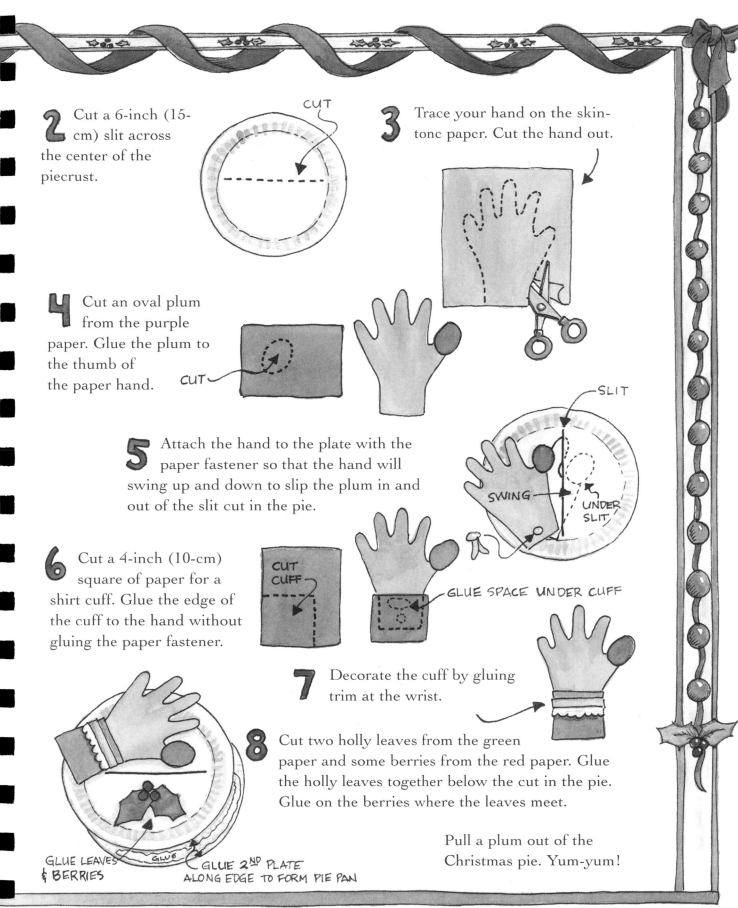

2 Cut a 6-inch (15-cm) slit across the center of the piecrust.

CUT

3 Trace your hand on the skin-tone paper. Cut the hand out.

4 Cut an oval plum from the purple paper. Glue the plum to the thumb of the paper hand.

CUT

5 Attach the hand to the plate with the paper fastener so that the hand will swing up and down to slip the plum in and out of the slit cut in the pie.

SLIT

SWING

UNDER SLIT

6 Cut a 4-inch (10-cm) square of paper for a shirt cuff. Glue the edge of the cuff to the hand without gluing the paper fastener.

CUT CUFF

GLUE SPACE UNDER CUFF

7 Decorate the cuff by gluing trim at the wrist.

8 Cut two holly leaves from the green paper and some berries from the red paper. Glue the holly leaves together below the cut in the pie. Glue on the berries where the leaves meet.

Pull a plum out of the Christmas pie. Yum-yum!

GLUE LEAVES & BERRIES

GLUE

GLUE 2ND PLATE ALONG EDGE TO FORM PIE PAN

"Wee Willie Winkie runs through the town . . ."

Wee Willie Winkie Nightcap

Here is what you need:

discarded adult-size tights or leggings

scissors

pipe cleaner

jingle bell

white glue

48

Here is what you do:

1 Cut one leg off the leggings or tights. If you are using tights, cut the foot off the other end. Trim the leg to the length you want the nightcap to be.

CUT HERE

STRING BELL

ANKLE END

WRAP PIPE CLEANER HERE

2 Close the leg at the ankle, using a piece of pipe cleaner with a jingle bell strung on it.

3 Fold up the other end of the leg twice. Secure the fold with small dots of glue in four places around the folded rim. Do not use too much glue or the cap will not stretch to fit over your head.

FOLD TWICE

GLUE SPOTS UNDER FOLD

Do you know why people wore nightcaps a long time ago?

"1, 2, 3, 4, 5. I caught a fish alive!
6, 7, 8, 9, 10. Then I let him go again!"

Key Fish Magnet

Here is what you need:

old keys

craft paint

paintbrush

white glue

GLUE

small wiggle eyes

sequins

sticky-back magnet

Styrofoam tray to work on

Here is what you do:

1 Turn the key sideways so that the handle becomes the head of the fish and the notched end the tail. Paint one side of the key and let it dry on the Styrofoam tray.

2 Glue the wiggle eye to the head of the fish, covering the hole in the key if it has one.

GLUE ON THE UNDER SIDE

3 Glue the sequin to the back of the top of the key so that it sticks out to look like a mouth.

4 Put a piece of sticky-back magnet on the back of the fish.

Make several key fish to swim on your refrigerator. Bubble, bubble!

Pick up Pizza

Teacher Meeting!

Call Mom!

Children's Songs

Bear Over The Mountain Puppet

Here is what you need:

 scissors

 gray and brown construction paper

 9-inch (23-cm) paper plate

 ruler

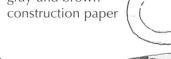 markers

 cereal box cardboard

 white glue

2 paper fasteners

dried coffee grounds

Here is what you do:

1 From the gray paper, cut a mountain shape large enough to cover the front of the paper plate.

2 From the brown paper, cut a bear shape about 5 inches (13 cm) long. Use the markers to give the bear a face. Cover the bear with glue and sprinkle on dried coffee grounds for fur.

3 Cut a strip from the cereal box cardboard that is about 8 inches (20 cm) long and 1 1/2 inches (4 cm) wide. Using a paper fastener, attach the bear through its center to one end of the strip.

4 Set the mountain shape on top of the paper plate. Push another paper fastener through the center of the mountain and the plate. Then push the fastener through the end of the cardboard strip.

The bear can now go up and over the mountain

"to see what he can see."

Old MacDonald's Barn

Here is what you need:

 newspaper to work on

scissors

 cardboard egg carton

 red and brown poster paint and a paintbrush

 white glue

 construction paper in several colors

 toilet-tissue tube

 large greeting card envelope

 markers

Here is what you do:

1 Paint the toilet-tissue tube red for the silo of the barn. If the envelope is not already red, paint that red, too.

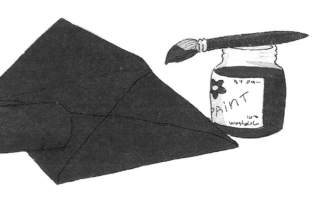

2 Cut one cup from the cardboard egg carton. Paint the outside of it brown. Glue the cup to the top of the silo.

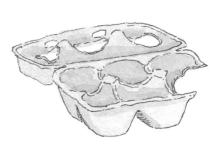

Here a moo, there a moo, everywhere a moo-moo. Old MacDonald had a farm, E-I-E-I-O

56

3 Open the flap of the envelope to form the roof of the barn. Glue the silo on one side of the front of the envelope.

4 Cut a double door and window for the barn from construction paper. Add details with the markers. Glue the door and window to the front of the envelope.

5 Draw all the animals on old MacDonald's farm on construction paper. Add details with the markers. Cut them out and slip them into the envelope barn.

As you sing the song "Old MacDonald Had a Farm" you can take each animal in the song out of the "barn" in turn.

Ee-i-Ee-i-oh!

A Pocket Full of Posies

Here is what you need:

 scissors

 white glue

kitchen-size paper cup

 old shirt with a pocket

 trim, ribbon, and lace

some real or artificial flowers

Here is what you do:

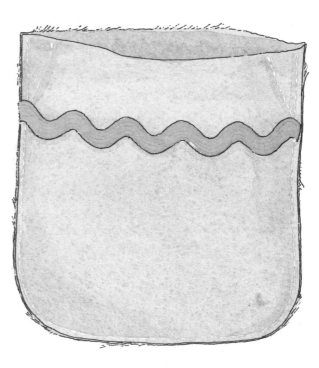

1 Cut the pocket off an old shirt. Decorate the pocket any way you wish, by gluing on trim, ribbon, and lace.

We all fall down.

Ashes!

2 Slip the paper cup into the pocket. The cup will make the pocket stand upright and also provide a container for the flowers.

3 Arrange real or artificial flowers in the pocket vase.

Put some stones in the bottom of the cup so the posies don't

"all fall down."

A Pocket full of posies

Ashes!

The Old Man is Snoring Puppet

Here is what you need:

 newspaper to work on

 7-inch (18-cm) paper bowl

 poster paint in skin tone and a paintbrush

 scissors

 white glue

 balloon

black and red markers

construction paper in skin tone

cotton balls

Here is what you do:

1 Paint the bottom of the bowl in the skin tone of your choice for the face of the old man.

2 Cut a nose shape from the construction paper. Poke a hole in the center of the bottom of the bowl. Glue only the top of the nose over the hole so that the nose covers the hole.

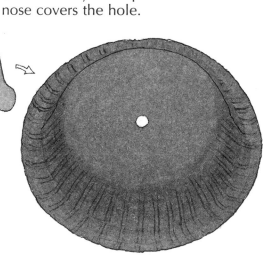

3 Use the markers to draw closed eyes and a mouth on the face.

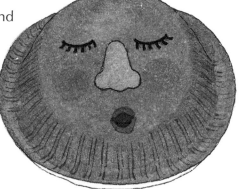

4 Glue cotton balls around the bottom rim of the face for a beard for the old man.

5 Push the open end of the balloon through the hole from the back of the face so that it is underneath the nose.

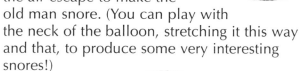

6 To use your pup-
pet, blow up the
balloon and slowly let
the air escape to make the
old man snore. (You can play with
the neck of the balloon, stretching it this way
and that, to produce some very interesting
snores!)

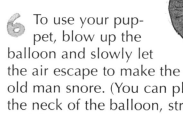

z z z z z z

61

Little star, How I wonder what you are!

Twinkle Star Finger Puppet

Here is what you need:

red permanent marker

unwanted shiny CD disk

scissors

white glue

2 large wiggle eyes

masking tape

Here is what you do:

1 Draw the shape of the star on the back of the disk with the marker, and then cut the star out. It must be cut with adult scissors, so you may need to ask a grown-up for help with this part.

2 Use the red marker to draw a smile on the shiny side of the star just below the hole.

3 Put a small strip of masking tape above the hole. Put a small piece of tape on the back of each wiggle eye. This will help create a better gluing surface between the disk and the wiggle eyes. Glue the eyes on to the star on top of the masking tape.

Put your finger through the hole from the back of the disk, so that your finger forms a nose for the star. Hold your star

"up above the world so high"

and watch the shiny surface twinkle.

Black Sheep Lapel Pin

Here is what you need:

 black 12-inch (30-cm) pipe cleaner

 black yarn

scissors

2 seed beads

 white glue

 thin ribbon

gold safety pin

Here is what you do:

1 Fold the black pipe cleaner into the frame of a sheep. Starting at one end, bend first one leg then the other. Fold the end down to make the back, then fold two legs for the front of the sheep. Bring the end up and fold it over to make the head. Trim off any extra pipe cleaner.

2 Tie one end of a long piece of yarn to the body of the sheep. Start wrapping the yarn around and around the body to fill the sheep out. If you run out of yarn before you think the sheep is plump enough just tie on another piece. Wrap the neck and top of the head a couple of times, leaving the end of the pipe cleaner head sticking out for the face of the sheep. Tie off the end of the yarn when you are done wrapping.

3 Tie a ribbon around the neck of the sheep.

4 Glue two seed bead eyes to the face of the sheep.

5 Slip the back of the safety pin under some of the yarn strands along the side of the sheep, so you can wear him on your collar.

This is a very tiny black sheep. He probably won't have

"three bags full"

of wool.

Jack-in-the-Box Pop-Up

Here is what you need:

   scissors

   white glue

   sliding matchbox

rubber band

blue construction paper

   trims

   markers

red yarn

Here is what you do:

1 Cut a strip of construction paper just big enough to cover the outside of the matchbox. Glue the paper around the matchbox.

Use the rubber band to hold the paper in place while the glue dries.

2 Decorate the outside of the box with bands of trim.

3 Use the markers to draw a face on the bottom of the inside box.

4 Cut bits of red yarn. Glue the bits to the top edge of the inner box above the face.

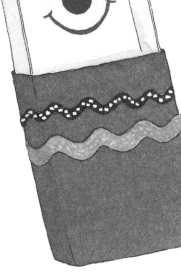

Slide the face inside the outer box. When it is time for Jack to pop out, just push on the bottom edge of the inner box.

"Won't you come out?"
"Yes, I will!"

67

Changing Face Cup Puppet

Here is what you need:

 scissors

 masking tape

 permanent markers

2 plastic cups

Here is what you do:

1 Cut out a circle, about the size of a half dollar, on the side near the bottom of one cup.

2 Wrap the bottom half of the second cup with masking tape.

1

2

3 Turn the wrapped cup over and place the cup with the hole over the wrapped cup. The hole will be the head. Draw a body under the head with permanent markers.

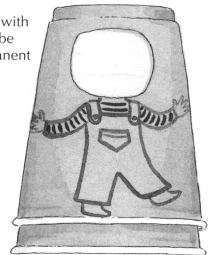

4 Draw a happy face on the masking tape showing through the hole for the head. Turn the outer cup just enough to hide the happy face and draw a sad face on the tape. Turn the cup again to draw a mad face and once more for a sleepy face. You will have room to draw just four faces. Do not turn the cup too far past each face or you will run out of space for the fourth face.

As you sing "If You're Happy and You Know It" turn the outer cup to show the correct face for each verse.

"If you're happy and you know it and you really want to show it..."

69

Green and Yellow Basket Necklace

Here is what you need:

 scissors

green labeling tape

 ruler

green pipe cleaner

 sharp markers

fabric scrap

yellow plastic lid

 yellow yarn

 paper

 white glue

pen

Here is what you do:

1 The yellow lid will be the basket. Add green to the basket by sticking a strip of green labeling tape around it.

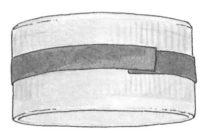

2 Cut a 6-inch (15-cm) piece of pipe cleaner for the handle. Squeeze glue into the bottom of the lid basket. Set the two ends of the pipe cleaner in the glue on each side of the basket.

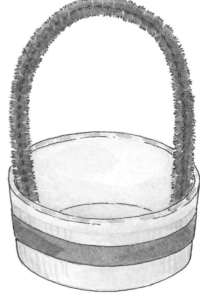

3 Cut a 3-inch (8-cm) square of fabric. Push the center of the fabric square down into the glue in the basket with the print side up.

Dear Sara, You're great! — Dan

4 Cut a small piece of paper for the "letter to my love." Write a little letter and decorate it with the markers. Fold the letter and put it in the basket.

5 Cut a 2-foot (61-cm) length of yellow yarn. String the yarn through the handle of the basket and tie the two ends together to form a necklace.

When you wear the green and yellow basket necklace, please be careful not to lose the letter! You might even want to glue it into the basket.

Finger Puppets of the Whole Family

Here is what you need:

 scissors

 white glue

 10 small beads and/or wiggle eyes

 5 tiny pom-poms

 trims

 yarn scraps

5 old neckties

 felt scraps

 ruler

5 small pom-poms

Here is what you do:

1 Cut a 2 1/2-inch (6-cm) piece off the narrow end of each of four ties. Cut a slightly longer piece off the end of the last tie for Tall Man. Each piece will be a finger puppet of one of the characters in the song. Use the widest tie end for Thumbkin, and the narrowest one for Pinky.

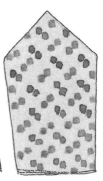

If any of the tie pieces have come open in the back, glue the seam back together.

2 Cut five 1-inch (2.5-cm) circles from different colors of felt for the faces. Glue a felt circle to each finger puppet, just below the start of the point. Glue two beads or wiggle eyes on each face. Give each man a nose by gluing a tiny pom-pom below the eyes. Give some of the puppets hair by gluing on yarn bits.

3 Glue a different piece of trim across the top of each head to form the bottom of the hat. Glue a small pom-pom to the point of each hat.

Put the appropriate puppet on each of the fingers of your left hand and hide them behind your back and sing

"Where is Thumbkin?"
"Here I am!"

Rocking Baby Toy

Here is what you need:

 scissors

 ruler

 white glue

newspaper to work on

 2 small wiggle eyes

green yarn

2 cotton balls

pink pom-pom

fabric scrap

thin pink ribbon

brown poster paint and a paintbrush

cardboard egg carton

old glove

brown construction paper

Here is what you do:

1 The glove will form the branches of a tree. Cut a 7-inch (18-cm) trunk for the tree from the brown paper. Glue the top of the trunk to the cuff of the glove.

2 Cut lots of yarn bits from the green yarn. Glue the yarn bits all over the glove and the top of the trunk for the leaves of the tree. Let the glue dry completely before putting the glove tree on your hand.

3 To make a cradle for the baby, cut two egg cups from the cardboard egg carton. Paint both cups brown, inside and out.

4 Cut a 10-inch (25-cm) length of thin pink ribbon. Tie the two ends together. Glue the knot over the bottom of one of the egg cups. Turn the second cup on its side and glue it inside one end of the bottom cup, over pink ribbon, to form the top of the cradle.

5 Glue two cotton balls in the cradle. Glue a scrap of fabric over the cotton to look like a blanket. Glue the pink pom-pom at the end of the blanket to make the head of the baby. Glue two wiggle eyes on the head.

To use the "Rock-a-bye Baby" toy, put the glove tree on one hand. Hang the cradle by the ribbon from one of the finger branches of the tree. Rock the cradle, then bend your finger down to make the cradle fall and

"...down will come baby, cradle, and all."

Farmer and Friends in the Dell

Here is what you need:

large sheet of green-construction paper

large sheet of white construction paper

scissors

cellophane tape

markers

Here is what you do:

1 Fold the white sheet of construction paper in half lengthwise and cut it in half on the line.

2 Draw all the characters from the song on one of the strips. You will need to draw the farmer, his wife, the child, the nurse, the dog, the cat, the rat, and the cheese. You need to start on the right side of the strip and draw them in order, going from right to left.

3 A dell is a small valley, usually with trees in it. On the green paper, draw an outdoor scene of what you think the farmer's dell might look like.

4 Cut a 6 1/2-inch (16.5-cm)-long slit 1 inch (2.5 cm) from each side of the green paper.

5 Tape the second strip of white paper to the right side of the paper strip with the characters on it. Thread the strip through the back of the green paper, across the front, and back through the second slit to form a continuous strip. Tape the two ends of the strip together on both sides.

Arrange the strip so that all the characters are at the back of the paper. As you sing each verse of the song, move that character through the slit to the front of the paper. For the last verse slide all the characters through the second slit to the back of the paper—except for the cheese, of course!

"The cheese stands alone."

Tippy Teapot

Here is what you need:

- scissors
- old knit glove
- masking tape
- 2 large wiggle eyes
- 6-inch (15-cm) paper bowl
- 12-inch (30-cm) pipe cleaner
- white glue
- 1-inch (2.5-cm) pom-pom
- trims
- red marker
- flower stickers

Here is what you do:

1 Cut the middle finger off the old glove. Use masking tape to attach the end of the finger to the rim of the bowl to form the spout of the teapot.

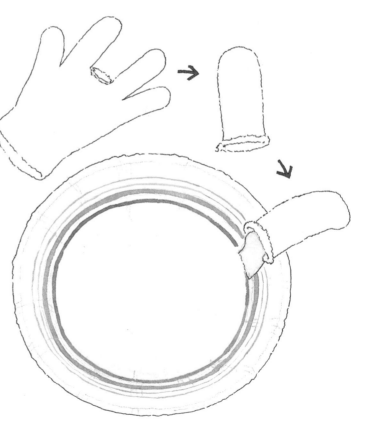

2 Bend the pipe cleaner in half. Twist it together to hold the fold. Tape the two ends of the folded pipe cleaner to the rim of the opposite side of the bowl to make the handle of the teapot.

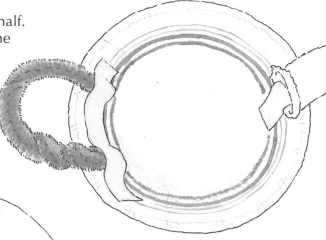

3 Glue the two wiggle eyes to the upper portion of the bottom of the bowl. Use the red marker to give the teapot a big smile.

4 Glue the pom-pom to the top edge of the teapot to look like the handle of the lid of the pot.

5 Decorate the teapot using trims and pretty flower stickers.

Hold the teapot by the handle with one hand and put the pointer finger of your other hand into the spout.

"...tip me over, pour me out."

Your Own Pretty Horse

Here is what you need:

- 2 cotton balls
- white glue
- ruler
- knit glove
- scissors
- black yarn
- black permanent marker
- black felt scrap
- 2 small wiggle eyes

Here is what you do:

1 Stuff the two cotton balls into the end of the middle finger of the glove to form a head for the horse, with the unstuffed portion of the finger forming the neck. The remaining thumb and three fingers will become the legs.

2 Use the marker to draw nostrils on the end of the head. Glue on the two wiggle eyes, about 1 inch (2.5 cm) back from the nostrils.

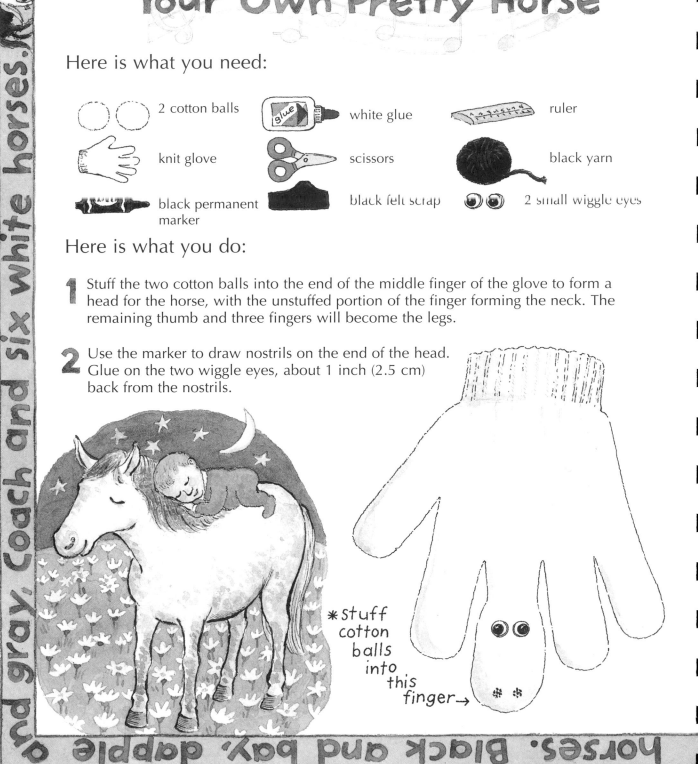

*stuff cotton balls into this finger→

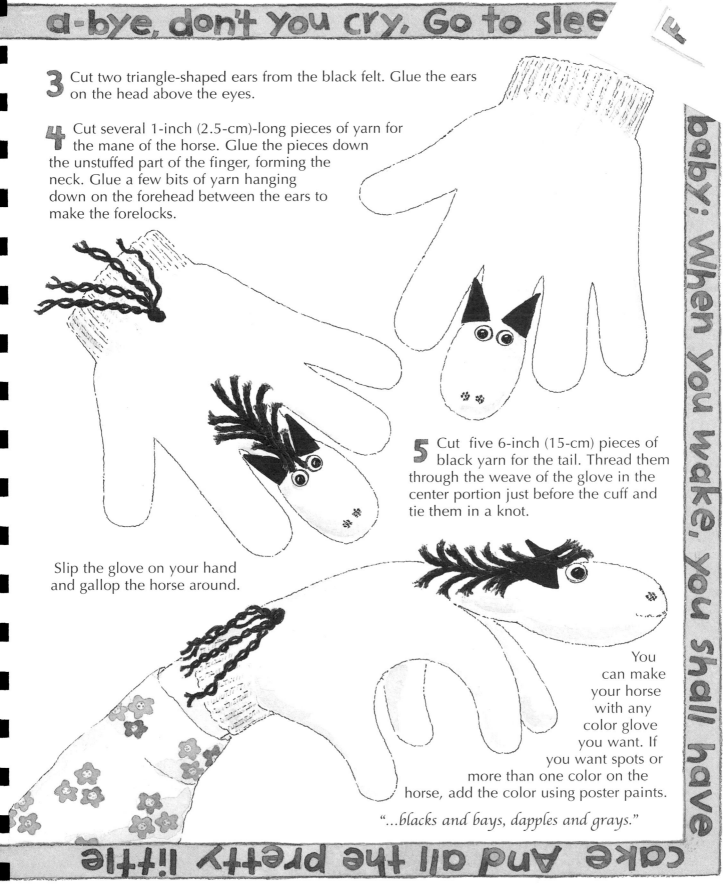

3 Cut two triangle-shaped ears from the black felt. Glue the ears on the head above the eyes.

4 Cut several 1-inch (2.5-cm)-long pieces of yarn for the mane of the horse. Glue the pieces down the unstuffed part of the finger, forming the neck. Glue a few bits of yarn hanging down on the forehead between the ears to make the forelocks.

5 Cut five 6-inch (15-cm) pieces of black yarn for the tail. Thread them through the weave of the glove in the center portion just before the cuff and tie them in a knot.

Slip the glove on your hand and gallop the horse around.

You can make your horse with any color glove you want. If you want spots or more than one color on the horse, add the color using poster paints.

"...blacks and bays, dapples and grays."

Bug Eating Frog on a Log

Here is what you need:

scissors

 black and brown markers

white glue

masking tape

green flip-open plastic top from salad-dressing bottle

6-inch (15-cm) red pipe cleaner

small card-board tube

2 small white pom-poms

seed bead

Here is what you do:

1 Cut down the side of the cardboard tube. Cut a 1-inch (2.5-cm) strip out of the side of the tube and discard it. The remaining tube will be the log for the frog. Use the brown marker to color it, or just add some lines to look like bark.

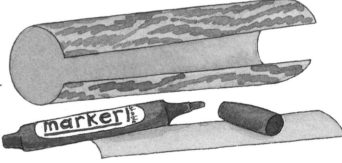

2 The green lid will become the frog. Put a small piece of masking tape on top of the lid to create a better gluing surface. Glue the two pom-poms on the top of the lid for the eyes. Use the black marker to give each eye a pupil.

3 The red pipe cleaner will be the tongue of the frog. Thread the seed bead onto one end of the pipe cleaner for the "bug" and fold the end down to hold it in place.

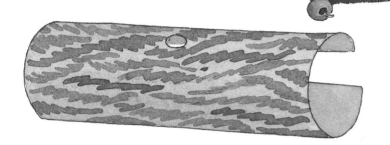

4 Hold the tube so that the opening is in the back. Poke a small hole in the center of the top of the tube.

5 Open the top of the lid to look like a frog with an open mouth. Use the masking tape on the back of the frog to tape it on the log, with the hole inside the lid directly over the hole in the log.

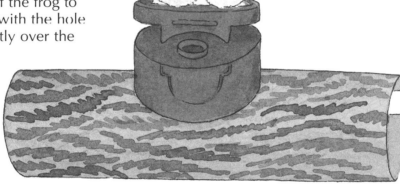

6 Thread the end of the pipe cleaner tongue without the bead down through the hole in the lid and the cardboard tube so that the end comes out behind the tube.

You should now be able to move the tongue of the frog in and out of the open mouth.

"...eating some most delicious bugs, yum yum!"

People on the Bus Going up and down

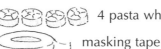

Here is what you need:

scissors

ruler

1 lb. spaghetti box

ballpoint pen

pipe cleaner

4 pasta wheels

masking tape

stickers

markers

clamp clothespin

white glue

labeling tape

paper

aluminum foil

Here is what you do:

1 Cut off the end of the spaghetti box so that the remaining part is 7 inches (18 cm) long and is the end with a window in it. This will be the bus.

2 Cover the bus with aluminum foil. Use masking tape to hold down the ends of the foil. Rub your finger over the foil until you find the window of the box. Rub around the window to make an outline of it in the foil. Gently go around the outline of the window with the point of the ballpoint pen to cut out the foil to expose the see-through window of the box.

3 Cut two 3-inch (8-cm) pieces of pipe cleaner for the wheel axles. Put a pasta wheel on each end and fold down the end of the pipe cleaner to hold each wheel in place.

Use the masking tape to tape the axles across the bottom of the bus, one toward the front and the other toward the back.

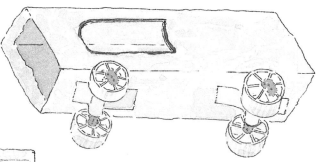

4 Decorate the bus with the labeling tape and stickers. If you want to draw something on the bus you will need to use permanent markers. Otherwise, put some masking tape over the foil and draw on the tape.

5 Cut a piece of paper that is a little wider than the window and twice as long. Fold the paper in half lengthwise. Along the top fold of the paper, use the markers to draw people looking out the bus window.

6 Glue the bottom fold of the paper to one side of the clamp clothespin. Glue the clothespin inside the open end of the bus so that the people are looking out the window.

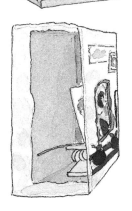

Pinch the end of the clothespin to move the people up and down.

"The people on the bus go up and down..."

Washed-Out Spider

Here is what you need:

- scissors
- short and long cardboard tubes
- black pipe cleaners
- black marker

- cellophane tape
- 1/2 (1.25 cm) inch wooden bead
- masking tape

- silver tinsel

- black yarn

- aluminum foil

Here is what you do:

1 Cut a slit halfway down the side of the short tube. Overlap the two sides of the cut tube and use the cellophane tape to hold the sides together. Slide the uncut end of the short tube up into one end of the long tube to look like the bent end of a waterspout. Tape it in place. If the short tube does not fit into the longer tube, just cut partway down the opposite side from the side you already cut, and overlap the cut ends to make it small enough around to fit inside.

2 Cover the entire tube with aluminum foil to make the waterspout. Use cellophane tape to hold loose ends in place.

3 Color the bead with the black marker to make the body of a spider. Put a small piece of masking tape on the side of the bead and draw two eyes.

4 Cut a 3-foot (91-cm) length of yarn. Tie the bead to one end of the yarn. Slide four 2-inch (5-cm) pipe cleaner pieces through the holes in the bead to make the eight legs for the spider.

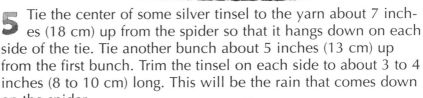

5 Tie the center of some silver tinsel to the yarn about 7 inches (18 cm) up from the spider so that it hangs down on each side of the tie. Tie another bunch about 5 inches (13 cm) up from the first bunch. Trim the tinsel on each side to about 3 to 4 inches (8 to 10 cm) long. This will be the rain that comes down on the spider.

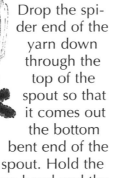

Drop the spider end of the yarn down through the top of the spout so that it comes out the bottom bent end of the spout. Hold the spout in one hand and the end of the yarn in the other hand. Start with just the spider hanging down out of the spout. Pull the yarn to bring the spider up into the spout. Lower the yarn to bring the spider and the rain down out of the tube. Pull the rain back up inside when the sun dries it, then, finally, pull the spider back up into the spout again.

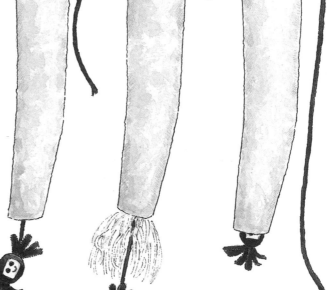

"Down came the rain and washed the spider out."

Find Bo Peep's Sheep Wheel

Here is what you need:

newspaper to work on

scissors

ruler

paper fastener

 2 paper plates, 9-inch (23-cm)

 markers

3 cotton balls

black pipe cleaner

 blue and green poster paint and a paintbrush

white paper

white glue

Here is what you do:

1 Paint the eating side of one of the paper plates blue for sky.

2 Cut a little less than half of the inner circle out of the second paper plate to create a window. Paint the eating side of the cut plate blue around the curved edge of the window and green for the grass below it. Let the plates dry.

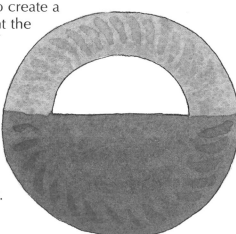
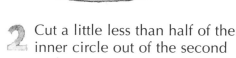

3 On the white paper draw a picture of little Bo Peep that is about 4 inches (10 cm) tall. Cut the picture out. Glue Bo Peep standing on one side of the green grass part of the cut plate.

4 Attach the cut plate over the blue plate by putting the paper fastener through the center of both plates.

5 Make sheep by gluing three cotton balls on the portion of the back plate showing through the window. Cut bits of black pipe cleaner for the head and legs of the sheep and glue them in place. Let the glue dry.

When the back plate is turned, the sheep can be hidden behind the first plate. They can be made to reappear by continuing to turn the back plate until they show in the window of the top plate again.

"Little Bo Peep has lost her sheep..."

BINGO Marker Can

Here is what you need:

 scissors

brown paper bag

 black marker

sticky-back magnets

 5 pry-off type bottle caps

black and white plus five other colors of construction paper scraps

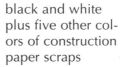 white glue

 small coffee can

 cellophane tape

 hole punch

Here is what you do:

1 Cut a piece from the brown bag big enough to cover the outside of the can. If the can has a paper label you can remove it and use it for a pattern. Otherwise, cut a piece that is slightly larger than the can, wrap it around the can, and trim it to fit. Use tape to hold the paper in place.

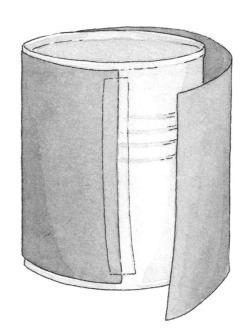

2 Cut two long, floppy dog ears from the brown paper to go on each side of the top of the can.

3 Fold the top end of each ear back and tape it inside the can to hold each ear in place.

4 Cut eyes from the white paper and pupils for the eyes from the black paper. Glue the pupils to the eyes, then glue the eyes on the upper portion of the can between the ears.

5 Cut a nose from the black paper and glue it on below the eyes. Use the marker to draw a mouth below the nose. Use the hole punch to make several "freckles" for each side of the face of the dog.

6 Cut a 1-inch (2.5-cm) circle from each of the five colors of construction paper.

7 Write one letter from the word B-I-N-G-O on each circle. Glue a circle inside each bottle cap. Cut a piece of sticky-back magnet for the back of each of the five caps and stick them in place.

Stick the caps on the front of the dog can to spell BINGO. As you sing the song you can remove a letter for each verse and drop it in the can. This can is also perfect for holding markers and other small items.

"...and BINGO was his name-o."

Children's Stories

Johnny Gruelle wrote the first Raggedy Ann
and Andy stories in the 1920s.

Raggedy Ann Pin

Here is what you need:

scissors

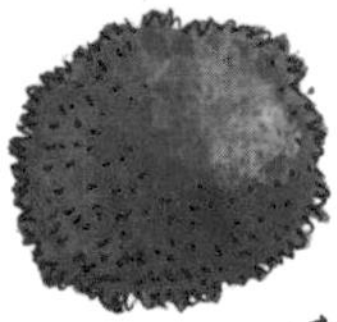

1-inch (2.5-cm)
red pom-pom

ruler

white paper scrap

red and black markers

two small black beads

white glue

large-size white rickrack

small safety pin

Here is what you do:

cut

1 Cut about one third of the fuzz
off the side of the red pom-pom.

2 Cut a 1-inch (2.5-cm) circle from the white paper.

3 Use the markers to draw a smile and triangle-shaped nose on the face. Glue the two black beads on the face for eyes.

4 Glue the head to the flat cut portion on the side of the pom-pom. Glue some of the red fuzz from the pom-pom trimming on the top of the head for bangs.

5 Cut a 1-inch (2.5-cm) piece of white rickrack for a collar. Glue the top of the rickrack behind the bottom of the head.

6 Attach a safety pin to the back of the head, and Raggedy Ann is ready to wear.

You might want to make a Raggedy Andy pin, too. Just cut a circle of blue felt for a hat. Glue a strip of white ribbon around the edge for the brim. Make the head just like the one for Raggedy Ann and add the hat.

Jean De Brunhoff's wonderful stories of
Babar the elephant inspired this next project.

Elephant Treasure Keeper

Here is what you need:

 newspaper to work on

blue plastic detergent
or softener bottle with
a handle

scissors

aluminum foil

masking tape

white glue

gold glitter

blue construction paper

cotton swab

two plastic wiggle eyes

small jar that will fit
inside the bottle

Here is what you do:

1 Soak the bottle in hot water to
thoroughly clean it and remove the
label. This will also soften the plastic and
make it easier to cut. Cut the bottom
part off the bottle so that the top is
left for the body of the elephant,
with the handle forming the trunk.

cut here

2 If you'd like a crown for your elephant, slip the inner spout out of the top of the bottle. Cover the outside of the spout with aluminum foil. Wrap the top portion of the outer rim of the crown with masking tape to create a better gluing surface. Cover the tape with glue and sprinkle it with gold glitter. Allow the glue to dry completely before slipping the spout back into the top of the bottle for a crown.

3 Cut two elephant ears from the blue paper. Use masking tape to attach one on each side of the handle that forms the trunk of the elephant.

4 Cut the cotton swab in half. Tape the two swab halves under the trunk of the elephant so that the cotton-wrapped ends stick out to form the tusks.

5 Put a small piece of masking tape on the back of each wiggle eye to create a better gluing surface. Glue the eyes to the front of the elephant above the trunk.

6 Hide the jar under the elephant.

This elephant will be happy to sit on your desk or dresser and hide secret stuff in the jar under him.

hide ➞

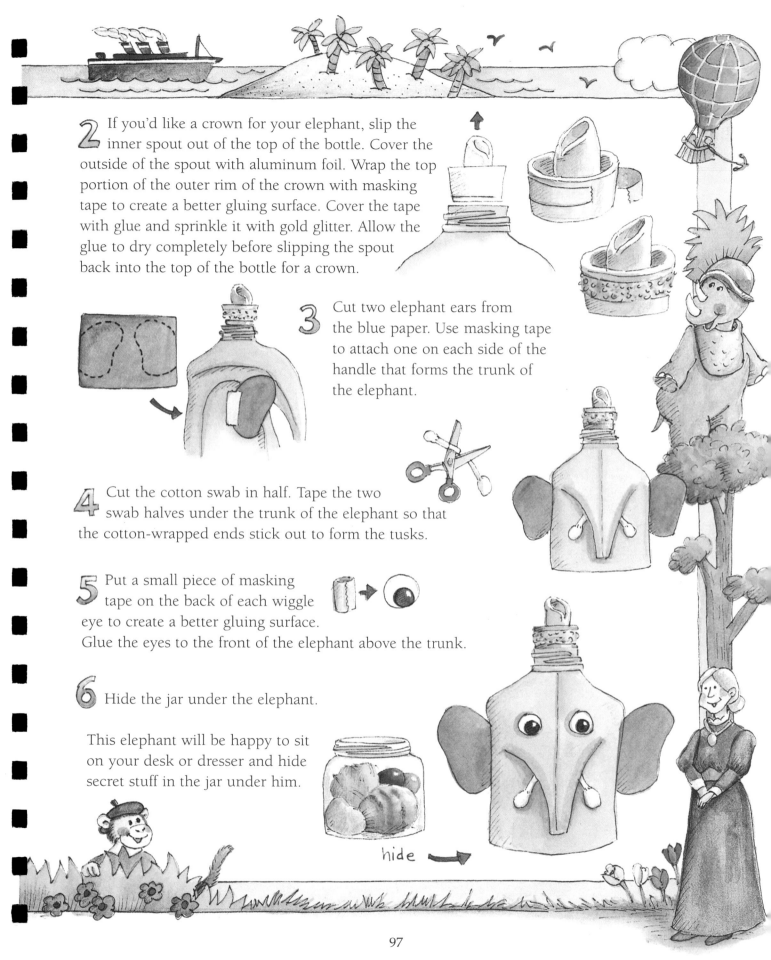

In Watty Piper's retelling of *The Little Engine That Could*, the positive attitude of the title character is what enables her to do what others could not.

Take the Toys up the Mountain

Here is what you need:

- newspaper to work on
- large 16-inch (41-cm) square or more piece of light-colored cardboard or poster board
- green and blue poster paint and a paintbrush
- stapler
- zipper long enough to reach diagonally across the cardboard
- white construction paper
- markers
- scissors
- white glue
- ruler
- pipe cleaner

Here is what you do:

1 Paint a slanted green hill that goes from the bottom left corner to the top right corner of the cardboard or poster board. Paint the remaining board blue for the sky.

2 Staple the ends of the zipper running up the hill, with the tab at the bottom. This will be the railroad track.

Staple

GREEN BLUE

3 On the white paper use the markers to draw any scenery you would like to have around the track. Cut the drawings out and glue them on the board.

4 Use the markers to draw on the white paper a picture of the little engine pulling the cars full of toys and treats. Make the train about 5 inches (13 cm) long. Fold the paper in half and cut around the train so that you have two sides. Decorate the part that will be the other side of the train.

fold

← cut line

5 String a 6-inch (15-cm) piece of pipe cleaner through the hole in the zipper tab. Wrap the ends around each other so that you have a piece about 4 inches (10 cm) long coming out from the tab.

6 Glue the two sides of the train together with the pipe cleaner in the middle so that the paper train sits on the zipper track. Starting at the bottom of the hill, you can help the little engine chug up the hill with the heavy load of toys for the children.

glue together

pipe cleaner

"I think I can, I think I can ..."

Mr. Bear knew exactly what any child's mother would want
for a present in Marjorie Flack's *Ask Mr. Bear*.

Bear Hug Puppet

Here is what you need:

sturdy, 3½-inch
(9 cm) paper cup

masking tape

yarn in your
hair color

markers

white glue

two party blowers

scissors

Here is what you do:

1 Turn the cup upside down. Poke a hole in
each side of the front of the cup to insert the
mouth end of the party blowers for arms.
Poke a larger hole in the middle center of
the back of the cup for the two ends of the
blowers to come out from the cup. Use
masking tape to tape the two ends of the
blowers together at the back of the cup.

holes

back

2 Wrap tape around the top part of the cup above the arms to create a face area. You can leave the face the shade of the masking tape or color it in your own skin tone.

3 Use the markers to draw a face on the front of the taped area just above and between the two arms.

4 Cut bits of yarn and glue them all over the top and sides of the cup for hair.

To show what Mr. Bear suggested as a gift for mother, blow on the party blowers and watch the puppet's arms stretch out to give a big bear hug.

The griddle used to cook Paul Bunyan's breakfast was so big that the cook put the butter on his feet and skated over it to grease it.

Grease Paul Bunyan's Griddle

Here is what you need:

- 9-inch (23-cm) paper plate
- aluminum foil
- stapler
- scissors
- ruler
- hole punch
- yellow felt scrap
- paper clip
- masking tape
- white paper
- markers
- white glue
- magnet

Here is what you do:

1. Cover the top of the paper plate with the foil, folding the edges down under the paper plate. Staple the foil to the plate all the way around the edges. Trim off all the extra foil under the plate that is beyond the staples.

fold edges over plate all around

plate bottom

staples

plate top

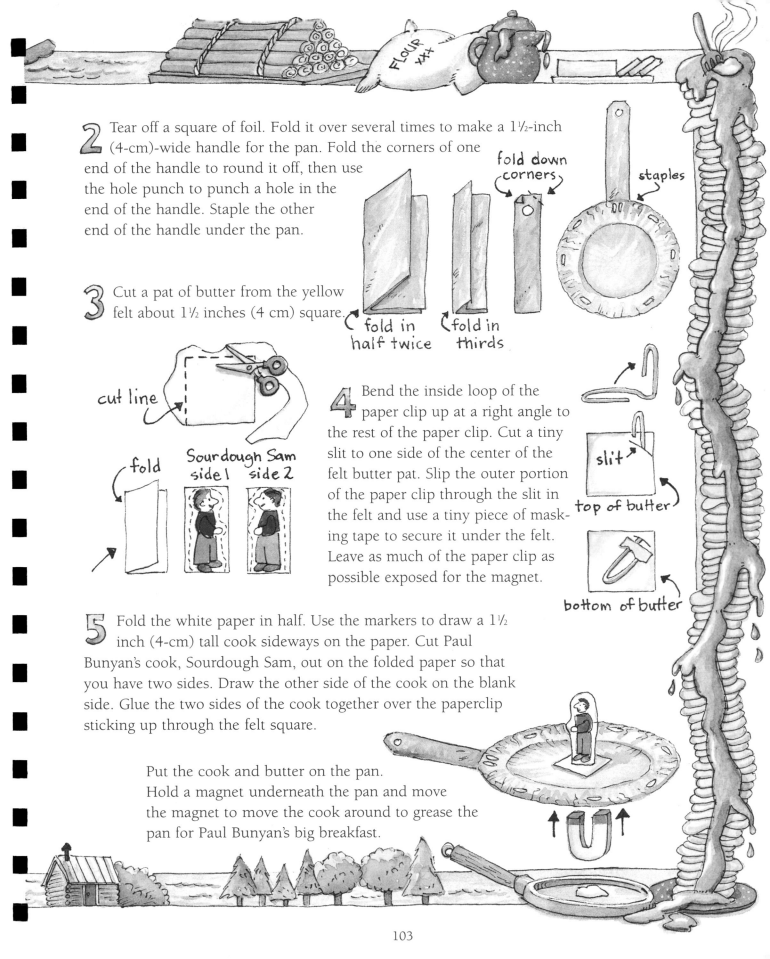

2 Tear off a square of foil. Fold it over several times to make a 1½-inch (4-cm)-wide handle for the pan. Fold the corners of one end of the handle to round it off, then use the hole punch to punch a hole in the end of the handle. Staple the other end of the handle under the pan.

fold down corners

staples

fold in half twice

fold in thirds

3 Cut a pat of butter from the yellow felt about 1½ inches (4 cm) square.

cut line

fold

Sourdough Sam
side 1   side 2

4 Bend the inside loop of the paper clip up at a right angle to the rest of the paper clip. Cut a tiny slit to one side of the center of the felt butter pat. Slip the outer portion of the paper clip through the slit in the felt and use a tiny piece of masking tape to secure it under the felt. Leave as much of the paper clip as possible exposed for the magnet.

slit

top of butter

bottom of butter

5 Fold the white paper in half. Use the markers to draw a 1½ inch (4-cm) tall cook sideways on the paper. Cut Paul Bunyan's cook, Sourdough Sam, out on the folded paper so that you have two sides. Draw the other side of the cook on the blank side. Glue the two sides of the cook together over the paperclip sticking up through the felt square.

Put the cook and butter on the pan. Hold a magnet underneath the pan and move the magnet to move the cook around to grease the pan for Paul Bunyan's big breakfast.

FLOUR xxx

In the story of *The Three Little Pigs*, the wolf keeps blowing the pigs' houses down.

Huff-and-Puff Wolf Puppet

Here is what you need:

 18 oz. (510 g) oatmeal box

 scissors

adult brown sock

 ruler

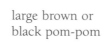 white glue

 large brown or black pom-pom

black marker

white construction paper scrap

 fiberfill

Here is what you do:

1 Remove the lid from the oatmeal box. Cut the bottom off the box.

2 Cut the end off the sock about 3 inches (8 cm) from the toe. Cut the 3-inch toepiece in half to make two ears for the wolf.

cut

3 Slide the cuff end of the sock over the box. Pull the end of the cuff over the open end of the box to form a mouth for the wolf. The open part of the sock should be hanging down from the other end of the box to form the neck of the wolf. This is where you will put your hand through.

4 Glue the pom-pom on the end of the box above the mouth.

5 Use the marker to draw two 1-inch (2.5-cm) eyes on the white paper. Cut the eyes out and glue them on the box above the nose.

6 Fold each ear piece in half and use glue to secure the fold. Glue the two ears on the head above the eyes.

fold

7 Stuff a handful of fiberfill into the box through the mouth.

mouth

fiberfill

To use the puppet, put your hand up through the neck to the inside of the head. Grab hold of the fiberfill. Support the head of the puppet with your other hand. As you say that the wolf "huffed" and "puffed," push the fiberfill out of the mouth slightly and then pull it back in. When he finally "blows the house down," push the fiberfill forward out of the mouth to look like a big gust of wind.

Better keep the wolf away from houses made of straw or sticks!

Because the little red hen did all the work by herself,
she also enjoyed the rewards of her work alone.

Little Red Hen Recipe Holder

Here is what you need:

- white glue
- red and yellow felt
- corrugated box cardboard
- pencil
- scissors
- wiggle eye
- 4 red feathers and 1 yellow feather
- large plastic laundry soap lid
- clay or Play-Doh
- plastic fork
- masking tape

Here is what you do:

1 Glue a piece of red felt larger than your hand to the cardboard and let it dry.

2 Trace your hand on the felt-covered cardboard. Cut the hand shape out. This will be the hen.

3 Cut a triangle beak for the hen from the yellow felt. Glue the beak on the end of the thumb. Glue on a wiggle eye above the beak.

4 Glue a red feather on each finger. Glue the yellow feather sideways across the hand for a wing.

masking tape

5 Fill the inside of the plastic lid with clay or Play-Doh. Stick the handle of the fork into the center of the clay. The prongs of the fork should stick up to hold a recipe card.

6 Put some masking tape across the side of the lid below the back side of the fork. This will create a better gluing surface for the hen. Glue the back of the hen over the tape, resting in the outer shelf portion of the lid.

The little red hen is always happy to help.

ChocolateChip Cookies
I bag of

The town mouse and the country mouse
discovered both the advantages and the disadvantages
of where each mouse lived.

Soft Sculpture Town and Country Mice

Here is what you need:

sheet of 18-inch by 12-inch (16 by 30 cm) gray construction paper

sheet of 18-inch by 12-inch (46-by 30-cm) brown construction paper

yellow, blue, pink, black, brown, and gray construction paper

stapler

scissors

white glue

ruler

two different 1-inch (2.5-cm)-wide ribbon trims

two plastic grocery bags

black yarn

black and pink 1-inch (2.5-cm) pom-poms

wheat stalk

Here is what you do:

1 The two large sheets of paper will form the heads for the two mice. Pull the sides of the sheet over each other so that the bottom of the paper comes to a point to form the nose of the mouse. Secure the paper with staples at the back where they overlap.

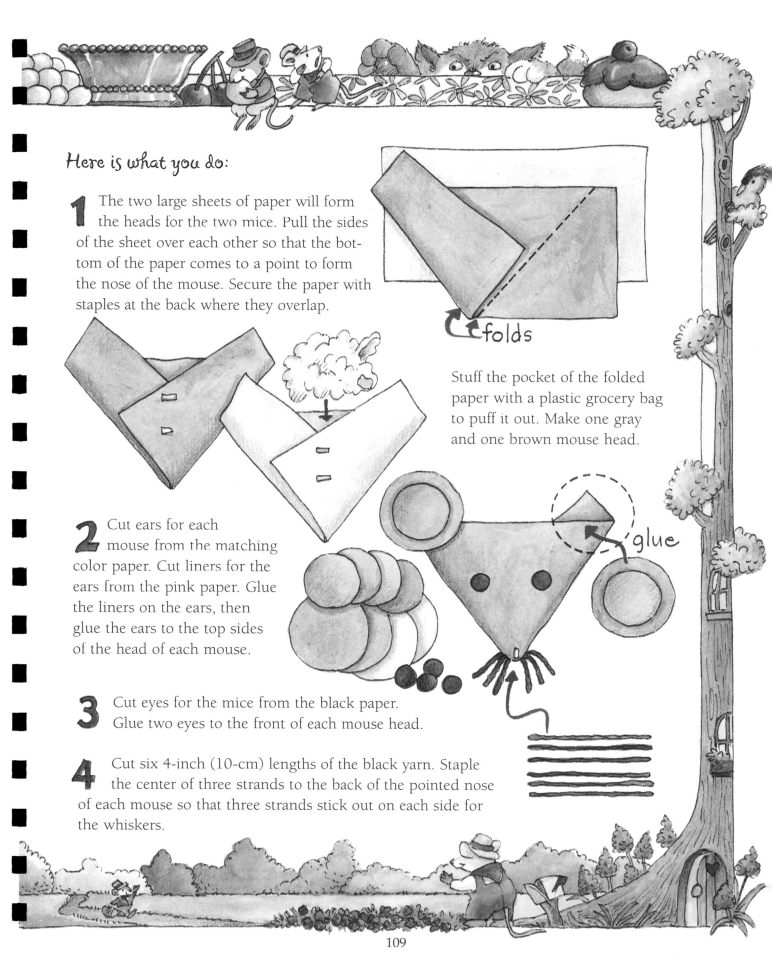

folds

Stuff the pocket of the folded paper with a plastic grocery bag to puff it out. Make one gray and one brown mouse head.

glue

2 Cut ears for each mouse from the matching color paper. Cut liners for the ears from the pink paper. Glue the liners on the ears, then glue the ears to the top sides of the head of each mouse.

3 Cut eyes for the mice from the black paper. Glue two eyes to the front of each mouse head.

4 Cut six 4-inch (10-cm) lengths of the black yarn. Staple the center of three strands to the back of the pointed nose of each mouse so that three strands stick out on each side for the whiskers.

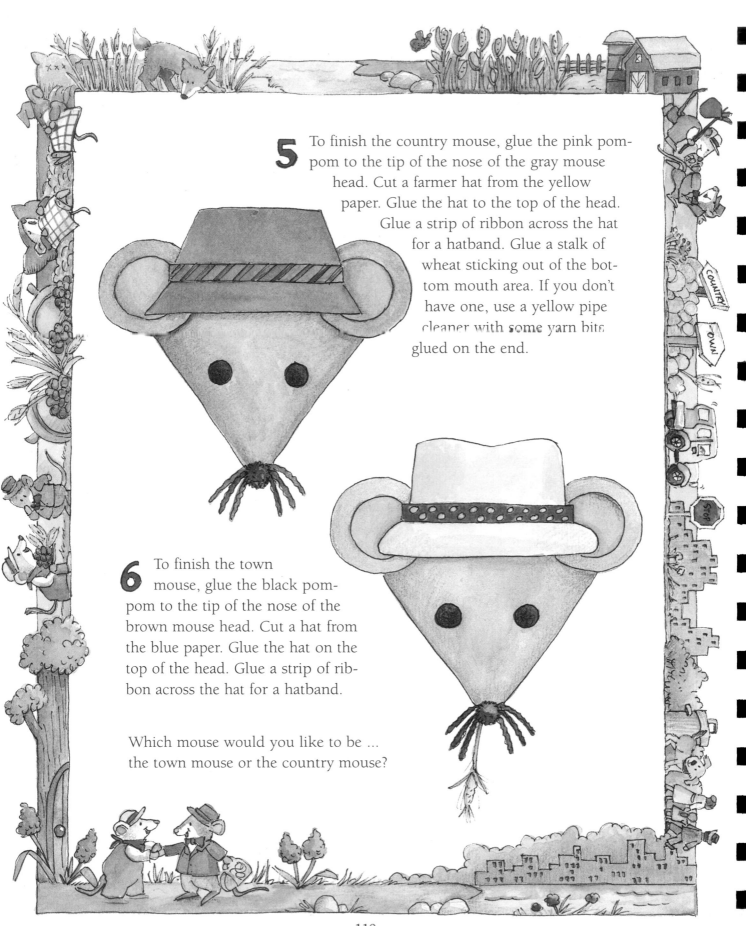

5 To finish the country mouse, glue the pink pom-pom to the tip of the nose of the gray mouse head. Cut a farmer hat from the yellow paper. Glue the hat to the top of the head. Glue a strip of ribbon across the hat for a hatband. Glue a stalk of wheat sticking out of the bottom mouth area. If you don't have one, use a yellow pipe cleaner with some yarn bits glued on the end.

6 To finish the town mouse, glue the black pom-pom to the tip of the nose of the brown mouse head. Cut a hat from the blue paper. Glue the hat on the top of the head. Glue a strip of ribbon across the hat for a hatband.

Which mouse would you like to be ... the town mouse or the country mouse?

In *The Tale of Peter Rabbit* by Beatrix Potter, little Peter gets into lots of trouble when he disobeys his mom!

Hide Peter in the Watering Can Puppet

Here is what you need:

golf tee

paper cup about 3½ inches (9 cm) tall

masking tape

aluminum foil

12-inch (30-cm) black pipe cleaner

two flexible straws

white glue

two large cotton balls

scissors

black and brown markers

hole punch

pink and white paper scraps

ruler

black yarn

blue felt scrap

gold sequin

Here is what you do:

1 To make the watering can, poke the golf tee into the side of the paper cup at an angle to look like a spout. Use masking tape to secure it on the inside of the cup. Cover the cup and golf tee with aluminum foil.

2 Fold the black pipe cleaner in half and twist the two halves together to make a handle for the watering can. Poke the two ends of the handle into the opposite side of the cup from the spout. Secure the ends inside the cup with masking tape.

3 To make Peter Rabbit, use masking tape to tape the two flexible straws together just below the bends.

4 Rub glue over the taped area. Slide the two cotton balls over the taped area by pushing the ends of the straws through the center of each cotton ball. The bottom cotton ball will form the body of the rabbit and the top one the head, with the two straws sticking out at the top for ears. Spread the two ears apart slightly.

5 Cover the front and back of each ear with a flat piece of masking tape. Do not wrap the tape around the ear, but rather allow the front and back tape to stick to each other on each side of the straw. Trim the tape so that it is pointed at the top like a rabbit's ear.

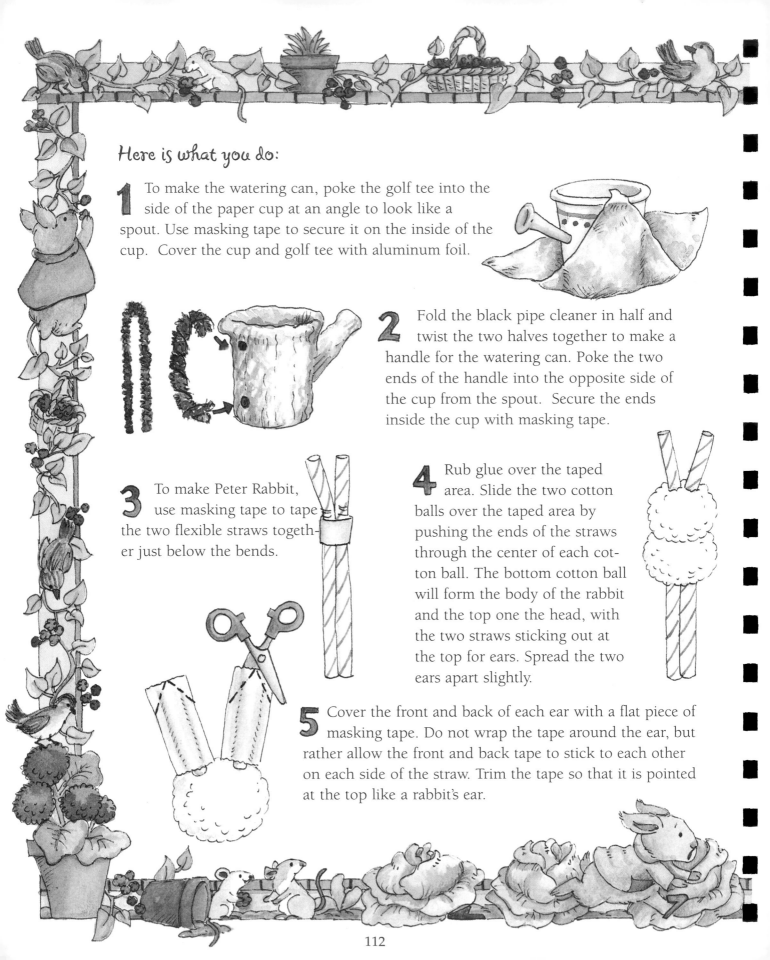

6 Use the brown marker to color the ears and the cotton ball head brown.

7 Punch eyes from the white paper. Use the black marker to give each eye a pupil. Glue the eyes to the head of the rabbit.

8 Cut a 2-inch (5-cm) length of black yarn. Knot the yarn in the center, then trim the ends to make whiskers about as wide as the rabbit's face. Unravel each strand of yarn. Punch a nose from the pink paper. Glue the whiskers to the face, then glue the pink nose over the center of the whiskers.

9 Cut a rectangle of blue felt wide enough to cover the rabbit's body and long enough to wrap around it for a little jacket. Glue the jacket wrapped around the body of the rabbit. Glue the gold sequin to the front of the jacket for a button.

10 Poke a hole in the bottom center of the watering can. Slide the end of the two straws through the hole from the inside of the cup, so that you can pop Peter Rabbit in and out of the watering can.

Quick! Help Peter hide! Here comes Mr. McGregor.

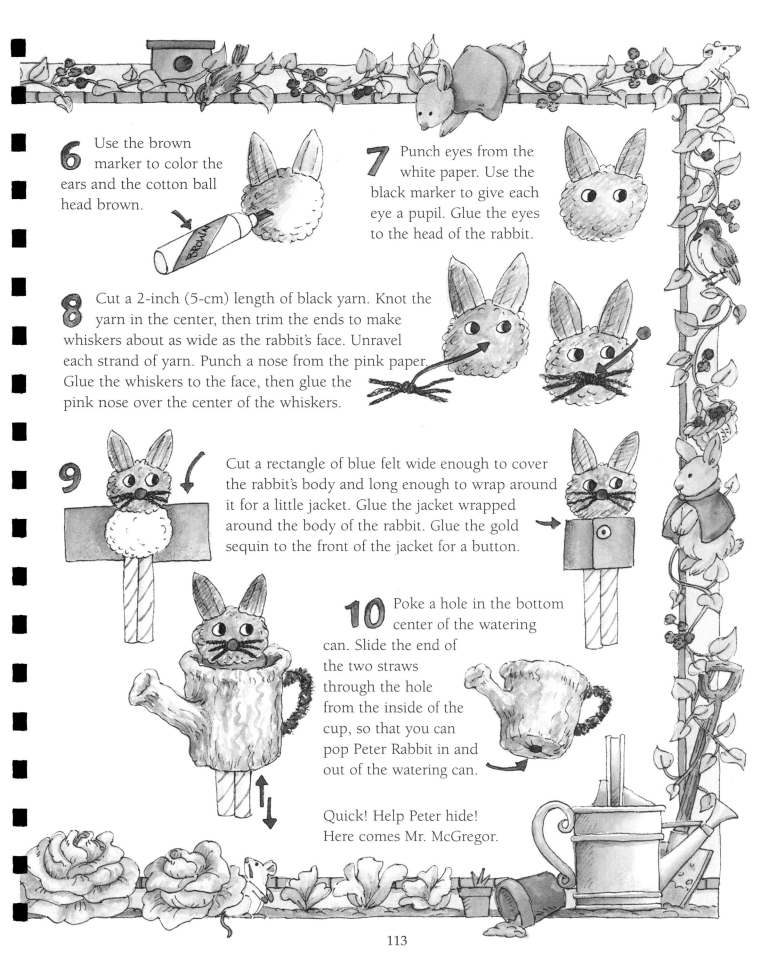

In *The Wizard of Oz*, Dorothy and Toto went to Oz in a spinning house.

Spinning House

Here is what you need:

scissors

½-gallon (2-liter) milk carton

ruler

string

large spool

white, blue, and red construction paper

white glue

markers

Here is what you do:

1 Cut the top off the milk carton about 3 inches (8 cm) down from the end of the spout. This will be the house.

2 Cut a 5-foot (1.5-meter) length of string. Poke a small hole in two opposite corners of the house, just below the end of the folded-in spout. Thread one end of the string through the hole on one side, into the house, and out the other hole. Thread the end of the string through the spool, then tie the two ends together.

3 Cut a strip of white paper to wrap around the outside of the house to cover it and overlap at each end. Glue the strip in place over the sides of the house. Cut a triangle of white paper to fit under each side of the roof to cover any print on the milk carton. Cut a piece of blue paper to fold over the top of the spout to cover it and hang out over each side to form a roof. Cut a chimney for the house from the red paper. Glue the chimney to the top of the roof.

4 Use markers and cut paper to add doors, windows, and any other detail you might want on the house.

To make your house spin off to Oz, hold the spool with one hand and twist the house around several times on the end of the string with your other hand. When you let the house go, it will spin on the end of the string.

Which of the three bears would you like to be?

Three Bears Family

Here is what you need:

scissors

markers

three large sheets of white poster board

Here is what you do:

1 Cut a hole slightly larger than your head in the top center of the poster board. You might want to use a plate as a pattern and trace around it.

2 Cut a smaller hole on each side of the poster board just below the center for your hands. You might want to use a large cup to trace around for a pattern. If the holes are not quite big enough for your hands, just trim a bit more off the edges until they feel right.

plate for tracing

cup for tracing

holes

3 Choose which bear you are making and use the markers to draw the bear on the poster board. The hole for your head should just be outlined and given bear ears. Add clothes below, with the arms ending in the two holes where your hands come through. Just draw the start of the legs where your own legs will come down to provide the legs for the character.

To use the bear costume, just put your hands through the back of the holes and peek through the head hole.

All you need is someone to be Goldilocks, and you can put on a play.

Peter Pan was a young boy who could fly!

Flying Peter Pan

Here is what you need:

- newspaper to work on
- masking tape 
- paper toy airplane 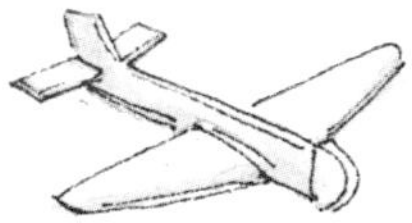
- green poster paint and a paintbrush 
- ruler 
- scissors 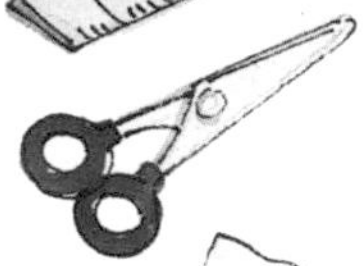
- white and green construction paper 
- white glue 
- red feather 
- markers 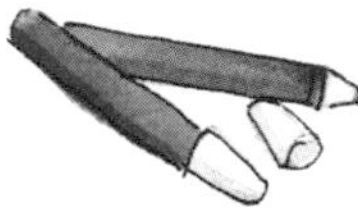

Here is what you do:

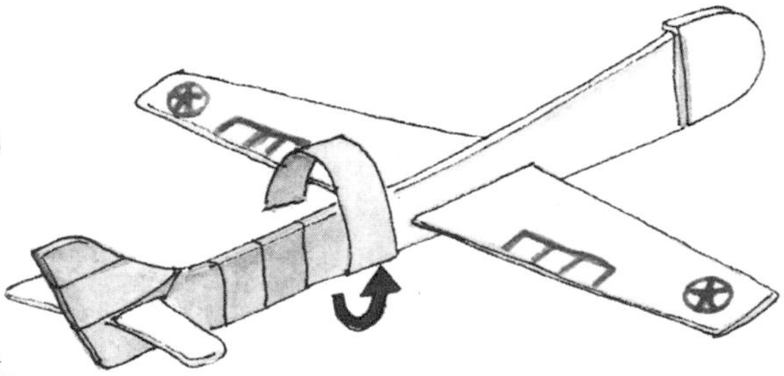

1 If the body of the airplane is Styrofoam rather then cardboard you will need to cover it with one thin layer of masking tape in order to paint it. Do not overlap the tape as this will add extra weight to the airplane and it will not fly.

2 Paint the airplane green. This will be the body of the flying Peter Pan.

3 Cut two identical 1½-inch (4-cm) circles from the white paper. Glue them together over the front tip of the airplane for the head. Cut two green triangles for the hat. Glue them together over the top of the head. Glue the red feather to one side of the hat.

fold paper in half to cut two of each

4 Draw a face on each side of the head with the markers.

5 Cut two hands from the white paper. Glue the end of a hand under the tip of each wing of the plane to make them look like outstretched arms.

fold

Fly Peter Pan just as you would a toy airplane. Don't throw him too hard or he may end up in Never Never Land.

119

When Pinocchio told a lie his nose would grow longer.

Growing Nose Pinocchio Puppet

Here is what you need:

newspaper to work on

2-inch (5-cm) Styrofoam ball

light brown poster paint and a paintbrush

ballpoint pen

scissors

green, white, black, and red construction paper

ruler

white glue

stapler

red feather

unsharpened pencil

Here is what you do:

1 Paint the Styrofoam ball brown and let it dry.

2 Use the pen to poke a hole straight through the center of the Styrofoam ball. This will be where the unsharpened pencil will go through to form the growing nose.

3 Cut two circles for eyes from the white paper. Cut two smaller circles from the black paper for pupils and glue one in the center of each eye. Glue the eyes on the Styrofoam ball head just above the nose hole.

4 Cut a smile from the red paper. Glue the smile on the head under the nose hole.

cut   staple

5 Cut a 4-inch (10-cm) circle from the green paper. Cut a slit from the edge to the center of the circle. Wrap one side of the cut circle over the other, overlapping by about 3 inches (8 cm), and staple the sides together to form a cone-shaped hat. Glue the red feather on one side of the hat.

To make Pinocchio's nose grow when he tells a lie, just push the pencil forward through the nose hole. Don't forget to always tell the truth!

Henny Penny was a little hen that mistakenly thought the sky was falling.

Hand Wings Henny Penny

Here is what you need:

newspaper to work on

scissors

ruler

corrugated cardboard

red poster paint and a paintbrush

red, orange, black, and white construction paper

white glue

red feathers

Here is what you do:

1 Cut a 15-inch (38-cm) circle from the cardboard. Cut a 3-inch (8-cm) circle out of the middle of the circle on each side so that your hands can slip through the holes to become the wings for Henny Penny.

2 Paint the front of the cardboard circle red.

3 Cut a 10-inch (25-cm)-tall head for the hen from the red construction paper. Cut eyes from the white paper and pupils for the eyes from the black paper. Glue a pupil in the center of each eye and glue the eyes on the head of the hen. Fold a piece of the orange paper in half and cut a triangle beak on the fold. Glue the back triangle only of the folded beak to the head of the hen so that the beak looks open.

fold

glue bottom only

4 Glue red feathers along the neck of the hen. Glue one red feather at the top of the head.

5 Glue the head to the top section of the cardboard.

fold

6 Cut two legs from orange construction paper. Glue them to the bottom of the cardboard.

Put your hands through the holes and flap them like wings as you tell all your friends that "the sky is falling."

You can use this same idea to make all the characters in the story of Henny Penny. If you make Foxy Loxy, just put socks over your hands to make them look like paws.

Cocky Locky   Ducky Lucky   Goosey Loosey   Turkey Lurkey   Foxy Loxy

The spoiled princess in the story *The Frog Prince* did not want to keep her promise to the frog.

Frog Prince Magnet

Here is what you need:

- newspaper to work on
- two wooden ice-cream spoons
- three green twist ties
- white glue
- green poster paint and a paintbrush
- scissors
- green and yellow felt scraps
- sequins
- masking tape
- two wiggle eyes
- thin red ribbon
- gold jingle bell
- piece of pipe cleaner
- piece of sticky-back magnet

Here is what you do:

1 With the bowl of one spoon as the bottom portion of the frog, glue one twist tie across the center to form the arms. Glue two more twist ties hanging down from the bottom to form the legs. Glue the second spoon over the first, with the bowl of the second spoon at the top of the frog for the head.

Glue top spoon to bottom spoon

Bottom Spoon

2 Paint the frog green.

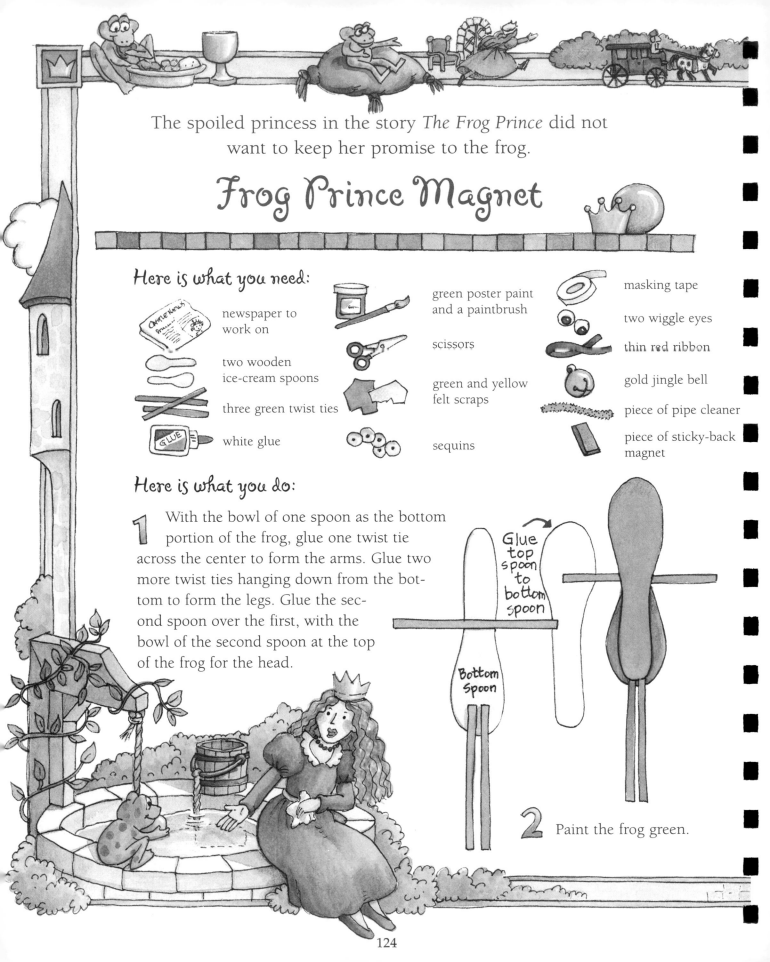

124

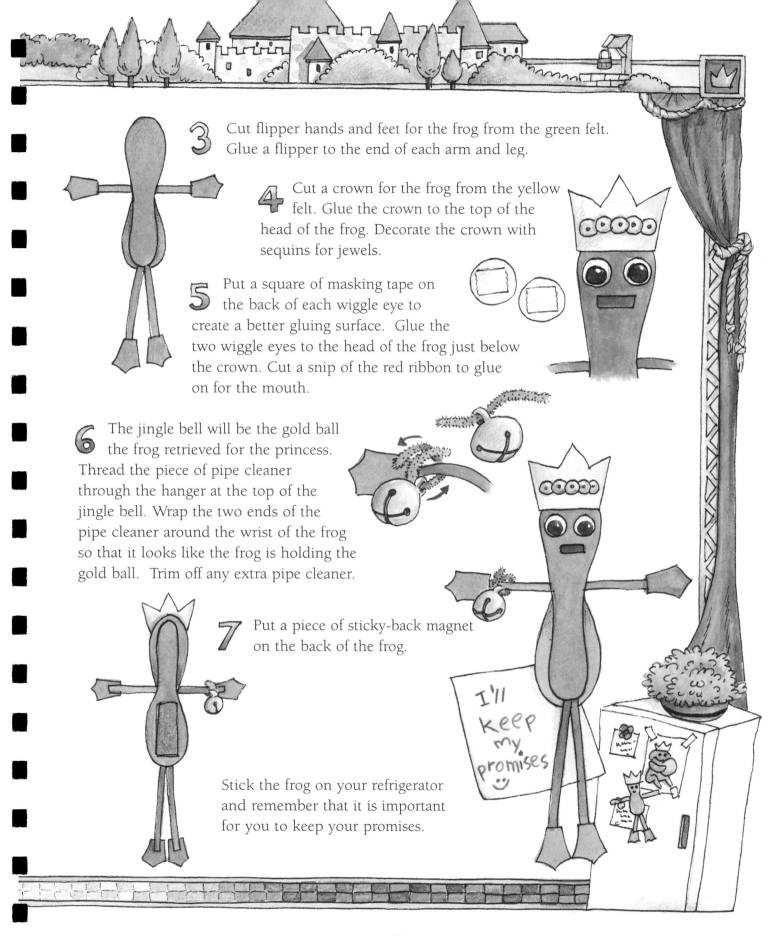

3 Cut flipper hands and feet for the frog from the green felt. Glue a flipper to the end of each arm and leg.

4 Cut a crown for the frog from the yellow felt. Glue the crown to the top of the head of the frog. Decorate the crown with sequins for jewels.

5 Put a square of masking tape on the back of each wiggle eye to create a better gluing surface. Glue the two wiggle eyes to the head of the frog just below the crown. Cut a snip of the red ribbon to glue on for the mouth.

6 The jingle bell will be the gold ball the frog retrieved for the princess. Thread the piece of pipe cleaner through the hanger at the top of the jingle bell. Wrap the two ends of the pipe cleaner around the wrist of the frog so that it looks like the frog is holding the gold ball. Trim off any extra pipe cleaner.

7 Put a piece of sticky-back magnet on the back of the frog.

Stick the frog on your refrigerator and remember that it is important for you to keep your promises.

I'll keep my promises. ☺

The gingerbread boy hopped right out
of the oven and ran away.

Running Gingerbread Boy

Here is what you need:

brown and green
construction paper

scissors

rickrack trim

12-inch (30-cm)
pipe cleaner

white glue

cellophane tape

pencil

markers

stapler

thin craft ribbon
spool

Here is what you do:

1 Fold the green paper in half. Trace around the
ribbon spool on the paper. Cut out the traced
circle on the folded paper so that you get two circles.
Glue a circle over each side of the ribbon spool to cover
it. Use the pencil to poke a hole through the paper on
each side to reopen the hole in the center of the spool.

trace around

fold

glue

2 On the brown paper draw one leg for the gingerbread boy as tall as
the distance from the center of the spool to the outside edge. Cut
the leg out and use it as a pattern to make a total of eight identical legs.
Glue four legs on each side of the spool, evenly spaced, with the tops
meeting at the outside edge of the hole at the
center of the spool.

pattern

side 1

side 2

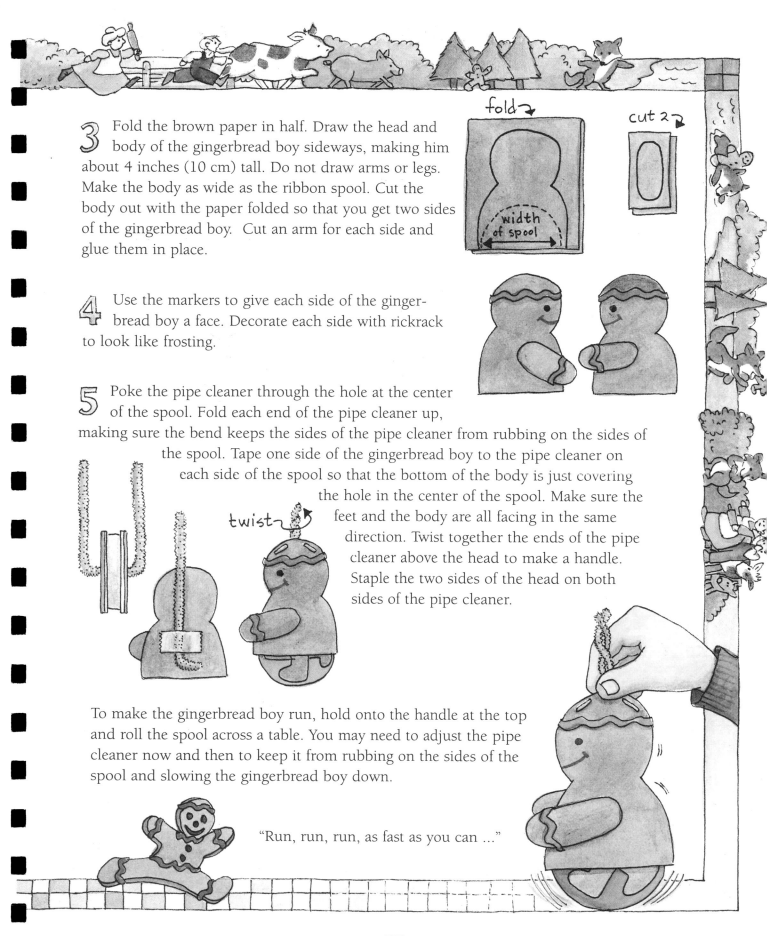

3 Fold the brown paper in half. Draw the head and body of the gingerbread boy sideways, making him about 4 inches (10 cm) tall. Do not draw arms or legs. Make the body as wide as the ribbon spool. Cut the body out with the paper folded so that you get two sides of the gingerbread boy. Cut an arm for each side and glue them in place.

fold

cut 2

width of spool

4 Use the markers to give each side of the ginger-bread boy a face. Decorate each side with rickrack to look like frosting.

5 Poke the pipe cleaner through the hole at the center of the spool. Fold each end of the pipe cleaner up, making sure the bend keeps the sides of the pipe cleaner from rubbing on the sides of the spool. Tape one side of the gingerbread boy to the pipe cleaner on each side of the spool so that the bottom of the body is just covering the hole in the center of the spool. Make sure the feet and the body are all facing in the same direction. Twist together the ends of the pipe cleaner above the head to make a handle. Staple the two sides of the head on both sides of the pipe cleaner.

twist

To make the gingerbread boy run, hold onto the handle at the top and roll the spool across a table. You may need to adjust the pipe cleaner now and then to keep it from rubbing on the sides of the spool and slowing the gingerbread boy down.

"Run, run, run, as fast as you can ..."

The tortoise showed the hare that slow
and sure can win the race.

Racing Tortoise and Hare

Here is what you need:

2 small toy cars

masking tape

fiberfill

white glue

green, brown,
black, and white
construction paper

scissors

black and pink
markers

hole punch

tiny pink pom-pom

larger white pom-pom

Here is what you do:

1 Cover the top of each of the cars with a
strip of masking tape to create a better
gluing surface.

2 To make the hare, glue fiberfill to the top of one car.
Pull some fiberfill down over each side of
the car, but do not obstruct the wheels.
This will be the body of the hare. Cut two
rabbit ears from the white paper. Color
the centers of each ear with the pink
marker. Glue the ears to the top front
of the car. Punch eyes from the black paper and
glue them on the front of the car. Glue the pink pom-
pom below the eyes for a nose. Glue the white
pom-pom on the back of the car for the tail.

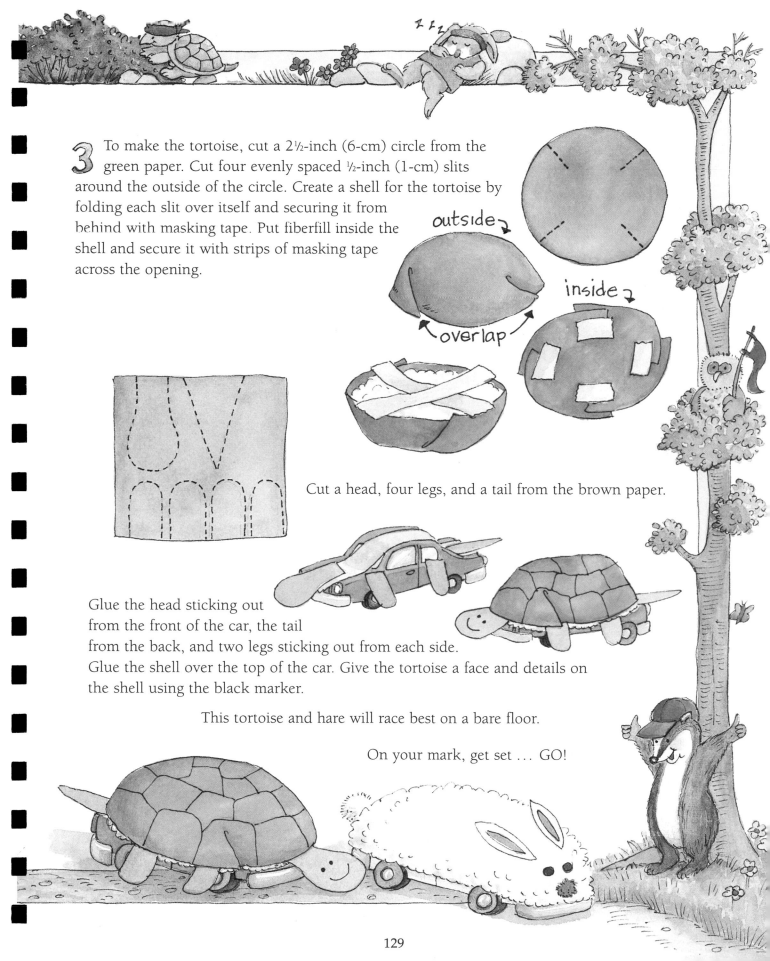

3 To make the tortoise, cut a 2½-inch (6-cm) circle from the green paper. Cut four evenly spaced ½-inch (1-cm) slits around the outside of the circle. Create a shell for the tortoise by folding each slit over itself and securing it from behind with masking tape. Put fiberfill inside the shell and secure it with strips of masking tape across the opening.

outside ↘

inside ↗

← overlap →

Cut a head, four legs, and a tail from the brown paper.

Glue the head sticking out from the front of the car, the tail from the back, and two legs sticking out from each side. Glue the shell over the top of the car. Give the tortoise a face and details on the shell using the black marker.

This tortoise and hare will race best on a bare floor.

On your mark, get set … GO!

Bambi, by Felix Salten, tells the story of a little fawn and his forest friends.

Bambi Puppet

Here is what you need:

lunch bag

scissors

1-inch (2.5-cm) black pom-pom

FIBER FILL — fiberfill

white glue

GLUE

black and brown construction paper

WHITE POSTER PAINT — white poster paint

Here is what you do:

1 Turn the bag so that the bottom flap is at the top. Fold the two corners of the flap in and secure them with glue to form the face of the puppet.

fold corners under

2 Cut two ears from the brown paper. Glue an ear on each side of the head. Cut two eyes from the black paper and glue them in place below the ears. Glue the black pom-pom on the bottom edge of the flap, between the two folded edges, for the nose.

3 Glue a thin layer of fiberfill on the front of the bag for the front of the fawn.

4 Turn the bag over. Dip your finger in the white paint and give the fawn fingerprint spots on the back.

To use the puppet, just slip your hand inside the bag and work the flap head up and down.

The white spots help a fawn hide from danger in the woods. Better give him lots of them!

In the Ukranian folktale, *The Mitten*, so many animals crawled into the mitten that it finally burst.

Bursting Mitten

Here is what you need:

scissors

two identical 16-oz. (454-g) sturdy plastic cups

wooden tongue depressor stick

masking tape

large knit mitten

seven or more pom-poms of various sizes and colors

hole punch

yarn pieces

paper scraps

white glue

Here is what you do:

1 Cut a hole in the bottom of one cup to slide the stick through. Cut an identical hole in the second cup. Cut the top off the second cup so that it is about 2 inches (5 cm) tall.

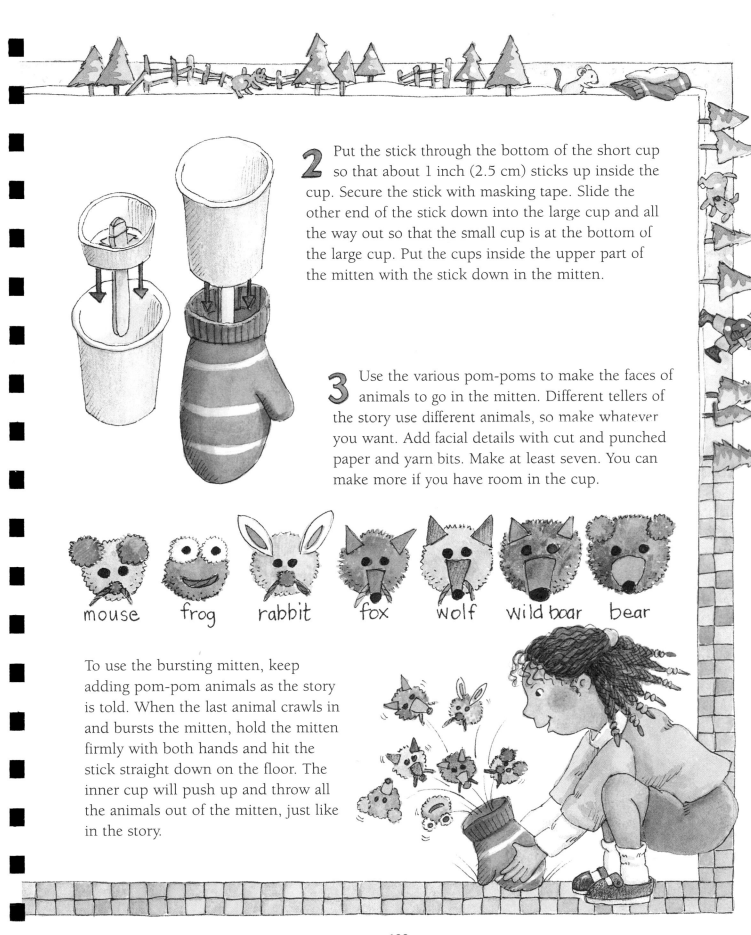

2 Put the stick through the bottom of the short cup so that about 1 inch (2.5 cm) sticks up inside the cup. Secure the stick with masking tape. Slide the other end of the stick down into the large cup and all the way out so that the small cup is at the bottom of the large cup. Put the cups inside the upper part of the mitten with the stick down in the mitten.

3 Use the various pom-poms to make the faces of animals to go in the mitten. Different tellers of the story use different animals, so make whatever you want. Add facial details with cut and punched paper and yarn bits. Make at least seven. You can make more if you have room in the cup.

mouse   frog   rabbit   fox   wolf   wild boar   bear

To use the bursting mitten, keep adding pom-pom animals as the story is told. When the last animal crawls in and bursts the mitten, hold the mitten firmly with both hands and hit the stick straight down on the floor. The inner cup will push up and throw all the animals out of the mitten, just like in the story.

In the Aesop's fable *The Crow and the Pitcher*, a smart crow solves the problem of how to get a drink.

Smart Crow Puppet

Here is what you need:

- ruler
- adult black sock
- stapler
- scissors
- yellow and white construction paper
- blue glue gel
- marker
- clear plastic cup
- water
- stones

Here is what you do:

1 The black sock will be the body of the crow. Turn about 3 inches (8 cm) of the sock toe in on itself to form a mouth. Separately staple the fold on the heel side and top side of the sock.

3"

fold inside

staples

2 Cut two identical 3-inch (8-cm) triangles for the top and bottom beak of the crow from the yellow paper. Glue a triangle beak over each staple on the top and bottom of the mouth.

3 Cut two eyes from the white paper. Use the marker to draw a pupil in the center of each eye. Glue the eyes on the heel side of the sock, just above the beak.

Fill the cup half full of water for the pitcher. Put your hand inside the crow puppet with your fingers on each side of the folded-in mouth. Have the crow keep picking up stones and dropping them in the water until the level rises enough to get a drink.

What a smart bird!

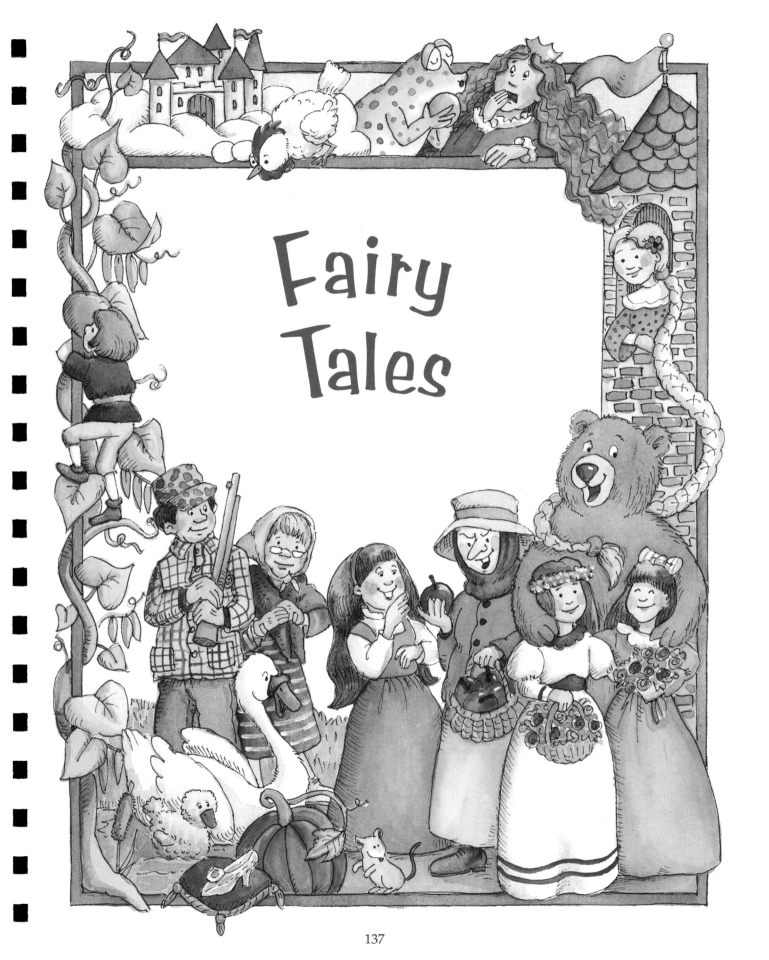

Fairy Tales

In **Snow White** and **Rose Red,** the beautiful sisters make friends with a talking bear. Do you know who the bear turns out to be?

Talking Bear

Here is what you need:

brown construction paper

pencil

black marker

Styrofoam tray

white glue

scissors

pinking shears

clamp clothespin

Here is what you do:

1. On brown construction paper, sketch a simple outline of a bear standing sideways.

Add details with a black
marker, but do not draw a
mouth. Cut the bear out.

2.

Use pinking shears to cut a
1-inch-long (2.5-cm) mouth
for the bear. If you don't have
pinking shears, try to cut a
zigzag opening with regular
scissors.

3. Rub glue along one side
of the top and bottom clamps
of the clothespin. Glue the top of
the bear's mouth to the top clamp
and its bottom jaw to the bottom
clamp. Break off some pieces of
Styrofoam to put between the
clamps of the clothespin while the
glue is drying. This will keep the
two sides of the clothespin from
gluing together.

When the glue has dried, the bear
will be ready to talk. Just squeeze
the end of the clothespin gently to
open and shut the bear's mouth.

In the story **Rapunzel,** a wicked witch keeps a young girl in a tower that can only be entered by climbing up her beautiful golden hair.

"Rapunzel in Her Tower" Puppet

Here is what you need:

cardboard wrapping paper tube at least 2 feet (61 cm) long and 2 inches (5 m) wide

black poster paint and a paintbrush

yellow and black yarn

white glue

pink construction paper

newspaper to work on

markers

scissors

Here is what you do:

1. Cut eight 1°-inch (4-cm) slits around one end of the tube to make eight tabs. Fold every other tab down to make the top of the tower.

2. Cut out a 3-inch-square (8-cm) window near the top of the tower.

3. Paint the tower black and let it dry.

4. Cut a circle face out of the pink construction paper to fit in the tower window. Use markers to draw the facial features of a pretty girl on the pink circle. Glue bits of yellow yarn around the face for hair. Glue the face to one side and the bottom edge of the tower window.

this long

5. Cut ten strands of yellow yarn about three times as long as the height of the tower. Fold the strands in half and knot the folded end. Braid the yarn until you have a braid that is slightly longer than the height of the tower from the bottom of the tower to the bottom edge of the window. Tie a piece of yarn around the end of the braid to hold it in place. Trim off any extra yarn at the end of the braid so that there is only about 1 inch (2.5 cm) of fringe below the tie.

6. Cut a piece of black yarn the same length as the braid. Tie one end through the top loop of the folded-over yarn of the braid. Drop the other end through the window of the tower so that it falls out the bottom of the tower. Tie that end to the bottom of the braid.

7. To work the puppet, slide the braid up inside the tower window so that it is hidden. Say, "Rapunzel, Rapunzel, let down your hair, so that I may climb your golden stair." Pull on the black yarn coming out of the window so that the braid appears and comes all the way down to the bottom of the tower.

In Snow White and the Seven Dwarfs

Snow White thought at first that the cottage filled with small furniture belonged to children.

Seven Sleepy Dwarfs

Here is what you need:

- two cardboard egg cartons
- corrugated box cardboard
- pink and blue poster paint and a paintbrush
- 14 wiggle eyes
- 7 small red pompoms
- fabric scraps in seven different patterns
- red construction paper
- red rickrack
- fiberfill
- scissors
- white glue
- newspaper to work on

Here is what you do:

1. Cut a two-section piece out of one of the egg cartons. Cut the top off the second egg carton. Turn the carton over to form the head and body of six dwarfs lying down.

glue & tape →

Glue the section cut from the other egg carton to one end to make seven dwarfs in a row. Paint all seven egg-cup dwarfs pink.

2. Cut a headboard and footboard for the bed just slightly longer than the row of dwarfs. The headboard should be about twice as tall as the footboard. Paint the bed parts blue on both sides and let them dry.

3. Cut a square of fabric for a blanket for each dwarf. Glue a blanket around the bottom egg cup of each dwarf.

4. Glue two wiggle eyes and a pompom nose on each top egg cup to make a face for each dwarf. Rub glue around each face and glue on a fiberfill beard and hair.

5. Glue the headboard across the top of the dwarfs and the footboard along the bottom. You might want to put the bed between two heavy objects, like books, to hold the pieces in place while the glue dries.

6. Cut a heart for each dwarf from red paper, and glue it on the headboard over each head. Glue a strip of rickrack across the footboard.

These seven dwarfs are all tucked in and ready for a good night's sleep after a day of hard work. "Good night."

The **Princess** and the **Pea** tells the story of the search for a true princess, the only one sensitive enough to feel a tiny pea through piles of mattresses and blankets.

Stapler Blankets

Here is what you need:

- scissors
- fabric
- yarn or thin ribbon
- fiberfill
- stapler and staples
- permanent markers
- white glue

Here is what you do:

1. Fold the fabric in half and cut out a piece of fabric in the size you would like the blanket to be. Remember, if you make it too large, you will not be able to get the stapler to the center of the blanket to "stitch" it.

2. Spread a thin layer of fiberfill between the folded fabric. Staple around the fabric at 1/2-inch (1.5-cm) intervals to "stitch" the blanket to hold the fiberfill in place. Staple a pattern of stitches across the blanket in both directions to give it a quiltlike appearance.

3.

If you have used a solid-color fabric, you can draw a picture in each square of the blanket, using permanent markers.

4. If you have used a patterned fabric, you can glue on knotted pieces of yarn or ribbon to accent the staple "stitches."

Make a pile of blankets for your doll friends. Stack them up with a dried pea underneath to see if you have a princess.

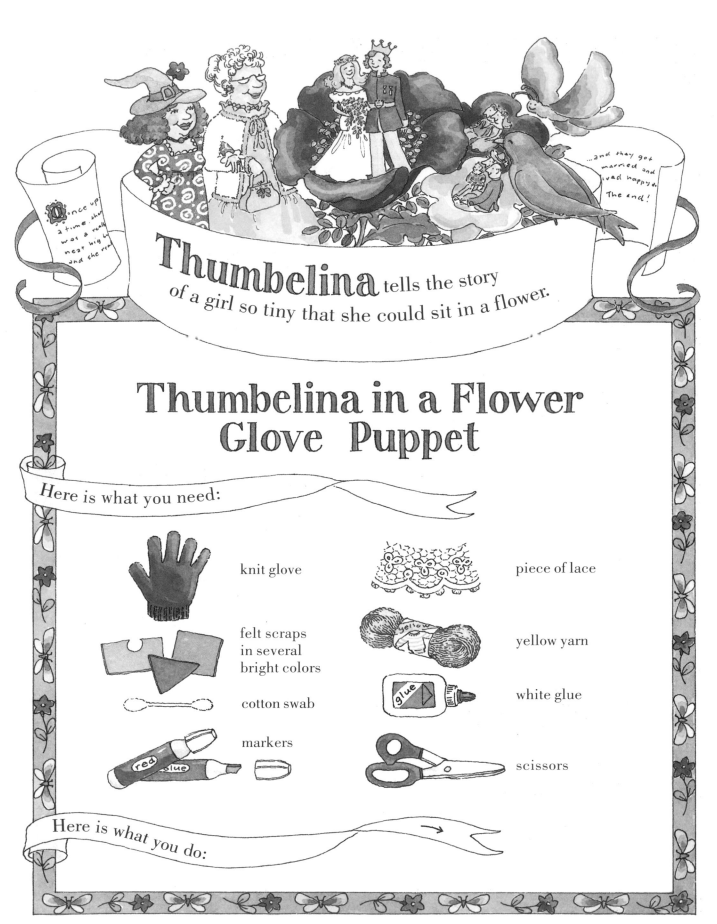

Thumbelina tells the story of a girl so tiny that she could sit in a flower.

Thumbelina in a Flower Glove Puppet

Here is what you need:

- knit glove
- piece of lace
- felt scraps in several bright colors
- yellow yarn
- cotton swab
- white glue
- markers
- scissors

Here is what you do:

1. Cut ten 3-inch (8-cm) flowers from felt of different colors. Cut a slit in the center of each flower so that it just slips over your finger. Slide two different color flowers about halfway down each finger of the glove.

10 –

2. Use the markers to draw a tiny face on one end of the stick that's left after cutting the cotton end off the swab. Unravel bits of yellow yarn and glue them around the face for hair.

3. Dip the opposite end of the swab in glue and tuck it down between one of the flowers and the finger of the glove. Dress the tiny girl by gluing on a piece of lace.

People will have to look very closely to discover which of the flowers in your garden is home for tiny Thumbelina.

Puss in Boots tells the story of a poor young man who receives a fortune through the cleverness of his cat.

Box Puzzle

Here is what you need:

nine small pudding or gelatin boxes of equal size

scissors

masking tape

white or colored paper

markers or crayons

white glue

Here is what you do:

1. Use masking tape to tape all of the boxes shut. Put strips of masking tape over the front of each of the boxes to create a better gluing surface.

2. On a sheet of paper, line up three rows of three pudding boxes, pushing them as close together as possible. Trace around the boxes on the paper. Trim the paper to exactly fit the boxes.

3. Draw your favorite picture from the story on the white paper.

4. Glue the paper to the nine boxes and let the glue dry.

5. Carefully cut the boxes apart to make a puzzle.

Mix up the box pieces of your picture and see if you can put it back together again.

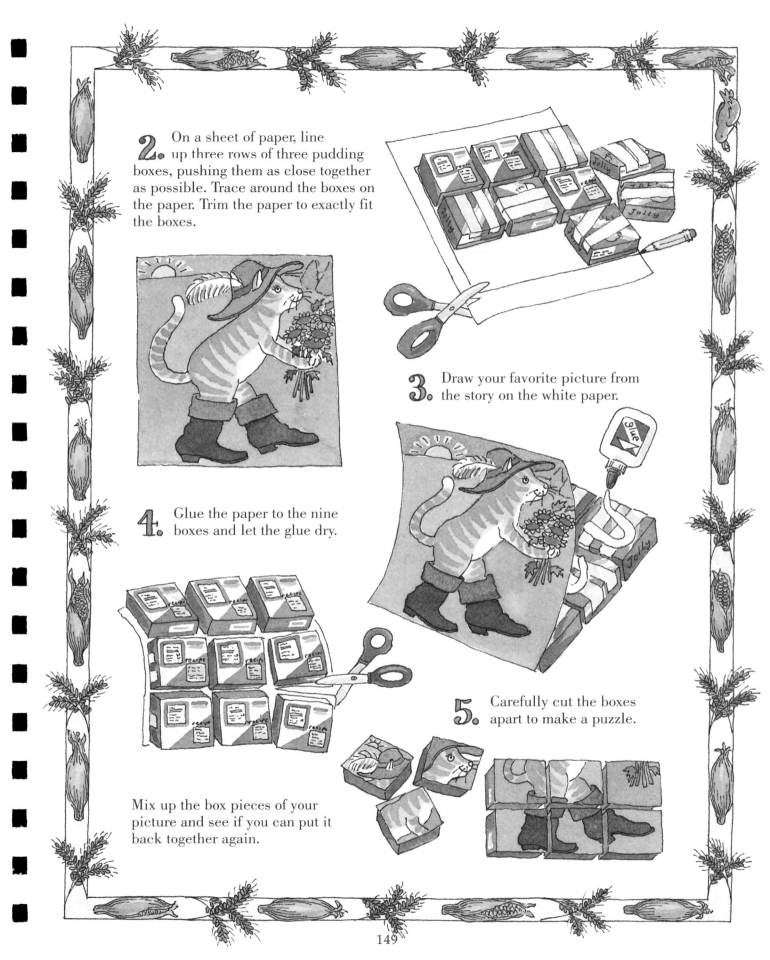

In **Cinderella**, a young girl goes from rags to riches when she wins the heart of a handsome prince.

Rags to Riches Cinderella

Here is what you need:

- light-colored poster board
- fabric scraps for a work dress and a ball gown
- pretty trim for the ball gown
- scissors
- white glue
- stapler and staples
- markers or crayons

Here is what you do:

1. Draw Cinderella from the waist up as she looked when she was a servant for her wicked stepmother and stepsisters. Use half of the poster board or less. Turn the picture upside down and draw another Cinderella with the waist starting at the end of the first picture. Draw this Cinderella with the top of a beautiful ball gown and her hair all done up for a party.

2. Cut two identical circles from the fabrics as wide as the height of both Cinderella halves. Make one circle out of dull fabric for her work dress. Make the other circle out of fancy fabric for the ball gown. Cut a slit in the center of each circle as wide as the waist at the center of the two dolls.

3. With the dull fabric circle on top and facing up and the fancy fabric on the bottom and facing down, slip the two skirts over the servant Cinderella's head. Staple the skirt around the waist.

4. Cut an apron from a fabric scrap and tie it around the waist of the skirt to cover the staples.

5. Turn the doll over to cover the servant doll and reveal Cinderella in her ball gown. Glue pretty trim on the gown to decorate it.

This flip doll lets you turn Cinderella's outfit from rags to a beautiful ball gown just like her fairy godmother did!

Little Red Riding Hood

tells of a little girl's encounter with a dangerous wolf as she goes through the forest to visit her sick grandmother.

Little Red Riding Hood Cup Puppet

Here is what you need:

- two red cups and one blue cup of the same size
- three paper fasteners
- brown yarn
- red ribbon
- red nail polish
- masking tape
- scissors
- white glue
- Styrofoam ball that fits in your cup
- pink poster paint and a paintbrush

Here is what you do:

1. To make the bottom of the cape, cut away about one third of one of the red cups, leaving the bottom of the cup intact. Turn the blue cup upside down for the dress and set the cut red cup over it for the bottom part of the cape. Poke a small hole through the bottom of the two cups.

152

2. Cut the top half off the second red cup. Line the inside of the cup with masking tape to create a surface glue will stick to. Turn the cup sideways to form a hood. Poke a hole through one side of the turned cup. Attach the turned cup to the body cups using a paper fastener pushed through the holes.

3. Paint the Styrofoam ball pink. Wrap a band of masking tape around the ball. Rub glue on the tape and glue the ball inside the hood for a head. Glue bits of yarn around the ball for hair. Push two paper fasteners into the head for eyes. Use nail polish to add pupils to the eyes, some rosy cheeks, and a little red mouth.

4. Tie a piece of ribbon in a bow around the neck of the puppet to make the tie of the hood.

Be very careful when taking your puppet for a walk in the woods!

In **Jack** and the **Beanstalk,** a boy climbs up a beanstalk grown from magic beans and finds the castle of a giant.

Climbing Jack Puppet

Here is what you need:

- shoe box
- cardboard paper-towel tube
- green tissue paper in one or more shades
- fiberfill
- green, blue, and black poster paint and a paintbrush
- scissors
- markers
- yarn

- yellow, blue, brown, and red construction paper scraps
- masking tape
- white glue
- pipe cleaner
- four cardboard toilet-tissue tubes
- newspaper to work on

Here is what you do:

1. Stand the shoe box up on one of the short sides. The top side will hold the castle. Cut away one third of the top to make an opening for the beanstalk.

If this seems to weaken the box, you can put a strip of masking tape across one side of the cut to help the box hold its shape.

2. Paint the bottom inside of the box green for grass. Paint the rest of the inside of the box blue for the sky. Paint the long tube green for the beanstalk. Glue the green tube in the box with the opening of the tube under the opening cut at the top of the box.

3. Cut a hole through the box under the tube and slightly outside the area under the tube. Cut a piece of yarn more than twice as long as the tube. Drop one end of the yarn down through the top of the tube. Drop the other end outside the tube and down through the hole that is sticking out from under the tube. Tie the two ends of yarn together to make a loop of yarn that will slide up and down the tube when you pull it from underneath the box.

4. Fold a piece of yellow paper in half. Draw a 2-inch-tall (5-cm) Jack on the fold. Color the picture and cut it out. Color the other side of the picture. Glue the two sides of the picture around the yarn so that it will go up and down the beanstalk when you pull the yarn.

5. Cut a tiny house from paper scraps. Add details with a marker and glue the house in one corner of the bottom of the box.

6. Cut leaves from the green tissue paper to glue on the beanstalk.

7. To make the giant's castle, paint four small tubes black and let them dry.

8. Cut eight 1-inch (2.5-cm) slits around the top of two of the tubes to make eight tabs. Fold every other tab in to make the tubes look like turrets of a castle.

9. Glue the four tubes together with the turrets on each side. Cut a door and windows from paper and glue them on the castle. Cut a paper flag and glue it to the end of a pipe cleaner. Glue the end of the pipe cleaner down in between the tubes at the top of the castle.

10. Cover the top of the box with masking tape to create a good gluing surface. Put strips of masking tape on the bottom of the castle. Glue the castle to the top of the box, beside the opening for the beanstalk. Glue fiberfill around the castle to look like clouds.

Send Jack up the beanstalk to pay the giant a visit.

In **Hansel and Gretel** two children lost in the woods come upon a gingerbread house beautifully decorated with candy.

Lunchbag Gingerbread House

Here is what you need:

lunchbag

scissors

cellophane tape

white glue

red and brown construction paper

four or more bottles of different-colored glues

newspaper

Here is what you do:

1. Stuff the lunchbag about three-quarters full with crumpled newspaper. Fold over the top and tape it shut. This will be the house.

2. Cut a roof for the house from brown paper. Fold the paper in half and cut the roof out on the fold with half on each side of the paper. Glue the roof to the top of the bag with the fold forming the top of the roof.

3. Cut a chimney, door, and windows from the red paper. Glue the pieces in place.

4. Use the colored glue to decorate the gingerbread house with candies and squiggles of frosting.

This house looks good enough to eat!

In the story **The Golden Goose**, the poor boy wins the hand of the beautiful princess by making her laugh.

Sad Then Happy Princess

Here is what you need:

scissors

heavy 9-inch (23-cm) paper plate

white, red, and blue construction paper

black marker

paper fastener

aluminum foil

pink ribbon

yellow yarn

white glue

pink poster paint and a paintbrush

newspaper to work on

masking tape

Here is what you do:

1. Paint the bottom of the plate pink for a face. Let the paint dry.

2. Cut eyes from the white and blue paper. Glue the eyes on the face. Use the black marker to draw pupils on the eyes. Use the marker to draw a nose and eyelashes.

3. Cut a smile from the red paper. Attach the smile to the face with a paper fastener so that it can be turned upside down to make a frown.

4. Glue strands of yellow yarn around the face for hair. Make two long braids of yellow yarn to glue on each side if you wish. Tie pink ribbon around the bottom of each braid.

5. Fold a piece of aluminum foil in half, then fold it in half again so that the foil is four sheets thick. Cut a crown for the princess from the foil. Wrap the crown around the top of the head and tape the two ends in back of the plate using masking tape.

The boy with the golden goose turns this Princess's frown into a smile.

The Emperor's New Clothes

tells the story of a man whose foolish pride and vanity cause him to appear in public in his underwear!

File Folder Emperor

Here is what you need:

two file folders (you can use old ones)

scissors

markers

white glue

Here is what you do:

1. Draw the body of the emperor dressed in a fancy outfit on the front of one of the file folders.

2. Cut a head and feet for the emperor from the second file folder. Color fancy shoes on the feet. Color the face and hair of the emperor and a jeweled crown on the head.

3. Glue the bottom of the head to the back top of the folder so that it sticks out above the fancy outfit you drew. Glue the shoes to the bottom back of the folder so they stick out below the front of the folder. You now have an emperor dressed in his fancy clothes.

4. Open the folder up and draw the body portion of the same emperor wearing only his underwear.

How embarrassing!

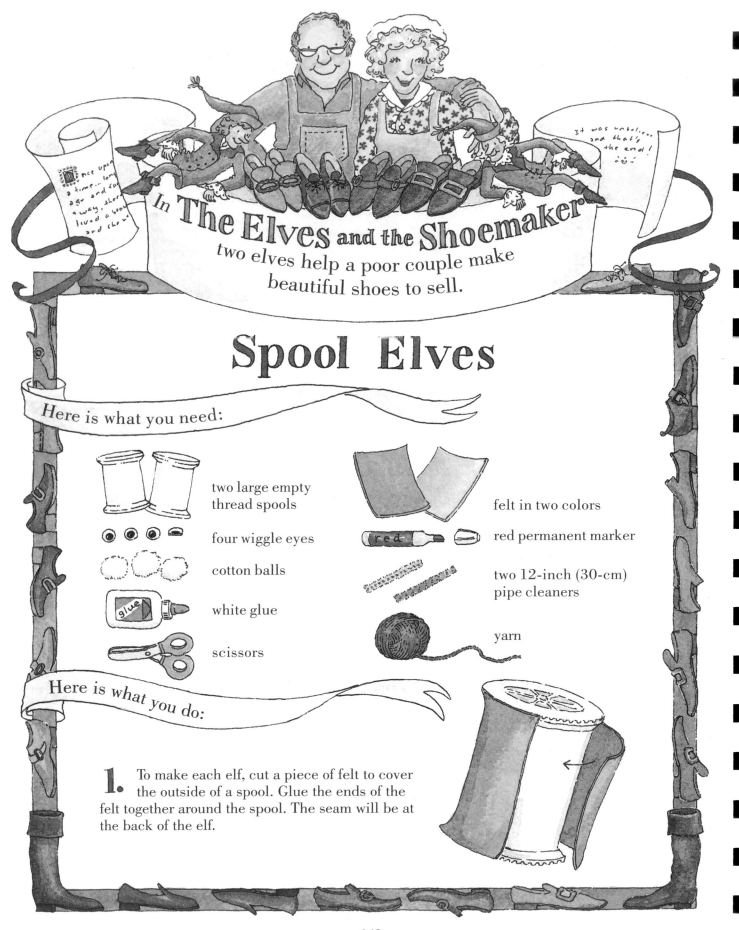

In **The Elves** and the **Shoemaker**

two elves help a poor couple make beautiful shoes to sell.

Spool Elves

Here is what you need:

two large empty thread spools

four wiggle eyes

cotton balls

white glue

scissors

felt in two colors

red permanent marker

two 12-inch (30-cm) pipe cleaners

yarn

Here is what you do:

1. To make each elf, cut a piece of felt to cover the outside of a spool. Glue the ends of the felt together around the spool. The seam will be at the back of the elf.

2. Cut a pipe cleaner in half. String the two pieces through the center of the spool so that equal parts of the two pipe cleaners stick out of each end of the spool. Bend the ends of the pipe cleaners coming out of the bottom of the spool to make feet. Fold the top two ends down over each side of the spool and then bend the ends out to make arms.

3. Tie a piece of yarn around the middle of the spool to hold the arms down and make a belt for the elf.

4. Spread out a cotton ball and glue it over the top, sides, and back of the spool for hair.

5. Glue on two wiggle eyes. Draw a smile with the red marker.

You might want to display your two elves in an old shoe with sewing supplies such as a needle, thread spools, and small scissors. Elves like to keep busy!

163

The Ugly Duckling tells the story of an awkward baby bird that grows into a beautiful swan.

Swan Puppet

Here is what you need:

- two 9-inch (23-cm) paper plates
- white adult-size sock
- black adult-size sock
- white and orange construction paper
- scissors
- black marker
- white craft feathers
- stapler and staples
- white glue

Here is what you do:

1. Fold two paper plates in half. Staple the edges of the two sides of the folded plates together. This will be the body of the swan.

2. Trace your hands on white paper. Cut the hand shapes out for wings. Glue a wing on each side of the plates. Glue some feathers on the wings.

3.

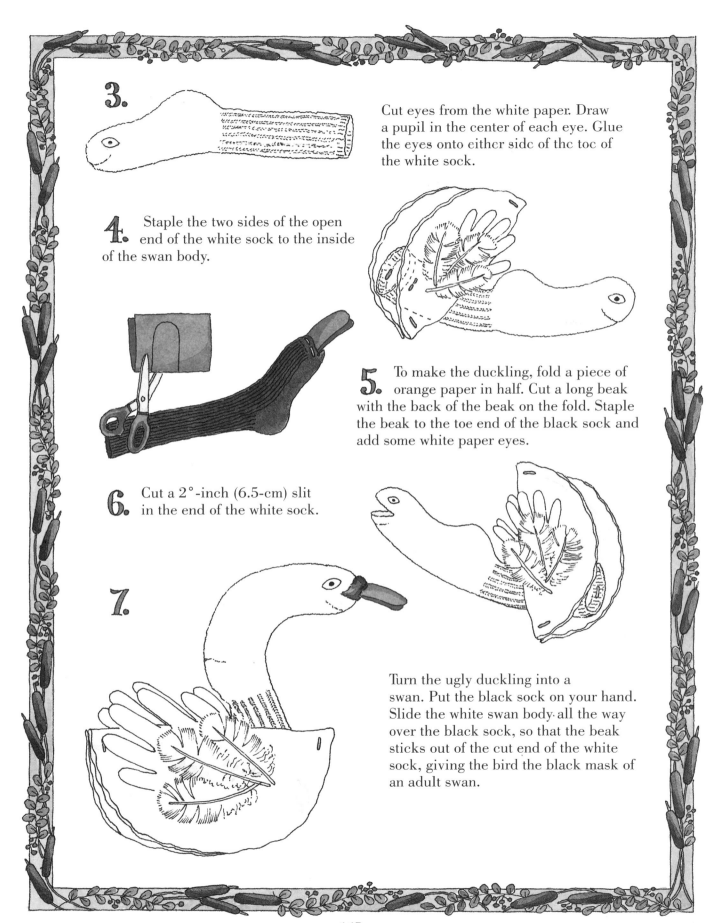

Cut eyes from the white paper. Draw a pupil in the center of each eye. Glue the eyes onto either side of the toe of the white sock.

4. Staple the two sides of the open end of the white sock to the inside of the swan body.

5. To make the duckling, fold a piece of orange paper in half. Cut a long beak with the back of the beak on the fold. Staple the beak to the toe end of the black sock and add some white paper eyes.

6. Cut a 2°-inch (6.5-cm) slit in the end of the white sock.

7.

Turn the ugly duckling into a swan. Put the black sock on your hand. Slide the white swan body all the way over the black sock, so that the beak sticks out of the cut end of the white sock, giving the bird the black mask of an adult swan.

In **The Fisherman and His Wife,** a man catches a magic fish that will give him three wishes if he agrees to let it go.

Magic Fish-in-the-Ocean Puppet

Here is what you need:

- shoe box lid
- blue poster paint and paintbrush
- small seashells
- green construction paper and bright-colored construction paper scraps
- clear bubble wrap
- thin string
- wide, clear packing tape
- gold glitter
- colorful pipe cleaner
- newspaper to work on
- hole punch
- scissors
- stapler and staples
- white glue

Here is what you do:

1. Cut a piece of string twice as long as the longest side of the box lid. Paint the string blue and paint the inside of the lid blue for the water and the sky.

2. Turn the lid so that it is as tall as it can be. Glue seashells along the bottom inside edge of the box to look like the ocean floor. Cut some seaweed from green paper and glue that along the bottom, too.

3. Cut fish from the brightly colored scraps of paper. Glue the fish in the bottom half of the box.

4. Cut a piece of bubble wrap just big enough to cover the bottom half of the lid with the ocean scene in it. Cut a wavy line across the top of the wrap to look like ocean waves. Staple the wrap to each side of the lid, over the ocean scene.

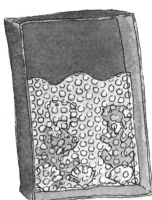

5. Cut a 6-inch (15-cm) piece of pipe cleaner. Bend it to make a fish shape, wrapping the two ends around each other to make the tail. Tie one end of the blue string to the top of the fish.

6. Cut a 4-inch (10-cm) piece of clear packing tape. Set the fish shape on the sticky side of the tape. Punch out an eye for the fish and set it on the tape. Sprinkle the tape with gold glitter. Cut another piece of tape and set it, sticky side to sticky side, on the first piece of tape so that the pipe cleaner shape is between them. Trim off the extra tape around the fish.

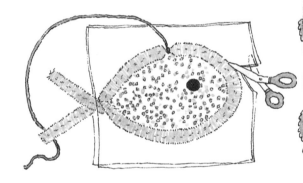

7. Punch a hole in the center top of the edge of the lid. Drop the fish down behind the bubble wrap and thread the other end of the string up through the hole at the top of the lid so that it hangs down behind the lid.

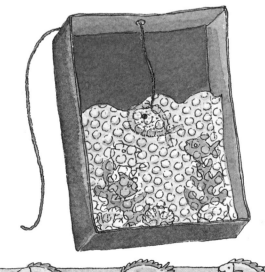

To make the magic fish swim in the ocean or come to the surface to grant a wish, just pull on the string.

In the story **Beauty and the Beast,** a beautiful young girl falls in love with a strange beast who turns out to be an enchanted prince.

Beast to Prince Doll

Here is what you need:

poster board

markers

paper fastener

scissors

Here is what you do:

1. Draw the head of the beast on poster board. Turn the head over and draw the neck and head of the prince attached to the beast head. Cut the two attached heads out.

2. Draw a body in fine clothing for the prince and the beast. Cut the body out. Use a paper fastener to attach the heads to the body so that one head shows above the shoulders and the other one is hidden behind the body.

3. Break the spell and change the beast back into the handsome prince!

4. You might want to make a beauty doll, too. You could make one face sad for when she thinks the beast is dying, and another face happy to use when she discovers he is the handsome prince.

The Frog Prince tells the story of a princess who did not want to keep her promise to a frog.

Frog Puppet

Here is what you need:

- two 9-inch (23-cm) paper plates
- red and green poster paint and paintbrush
- red party blower
- two large cotton balls
- black and green construction paper
- white glue
- scissors
- newspaper to work on

Here is what you do:

1. Paint the bottom of one plate green and the top of the other plate red and let them dry.

2. From the green paper, cut four frog legs about 5 inches (13 cm) long. Glue the bottom of the red plate to the top of the green plate. Fold the plates in half so that the red forms the mouth of the frog. Slide two frog legs in between the two plates on the bottom half of each side of the frog.

4 -

3.

Glue two cotton balls on the top green fold of the frog for eyes. Cut pupils from black paper and glue them on each cotton ball.

4. Cut a small slit in the center of the fold of the frog. Open the frog mouth and push the end of the party blower through the slit so that the mouthpiece sticks out in back of the frog and the curled part forms the tongue of the frog.

Surprise someone you know by blowing on the party blower to make the frog tongue pop out.

The story of **Rumpelstiltskin** tells of a little man with a very unusual name and the lady who had to guess it in order to keep her baby.

Story Box Theater

Here is what you need:

- small carton about 5 inches (13 cm) deep
- poster paint and a paintbrush
- white paper
- ribbon and trim
- markers or crayons
- two paper fasteners
- scissors
- thin cardboard
- old magazines and catalogs
- white glue
- newspaper to work on

Here is what you do:

1. Stand the carton on end so that the flaps open and shut like doors. Cut the other two flaps at the top and bottom off. Cut a 1-inch-wide (2.5-cm) slit down each side of the carton toward the back (which was the bottom) of the box.

2. Paint the entire box, inside and outside. Let the paint dry.

3. Push a paper fastener into the middle edge of each door. Tie a ribbon around one of the fasteners. To close the theater, just tie the ribbon to the other fastener to keep the flaps shut. Decorate the theater by gluing on the trims of your choice.

4. You will need to cut a sheet of thin cardboard for each scene you wish to include in the telling of the story.

The sheets should be a little shorter than the height of the slits in the side of the theater stage, but longer than the width of the box, so that the scenes can rest on the bottom of each slit.

5. Choose backgrounds for the story from old magazines and catalogs. The lady in *Rumpelstiltskin* was quite poor in the beginning of the story, so you might want to find an old barn picture for the background. Cover the sheet of cardboard with the magazine picture. You may need more than one picture. You can fill in with greenery for outside scenes, and extra walls and furniture for indoor scenes.

6. Draw a picture of the lady and her father on white paper, color the pictures, and cut them out. Glue these on the background picture. In the next scene, the poor lady is locked in a tower room in a castle. Try finding a large picture of a stone wall and use this to look like the castle walls. Finding the right background for each scene in the story can be both fun and challenging.

When you have completed all of the scenes in the story, you will be ready to tell the tale. You can use your scenes to tell the story for your own enjoyment or for that of others. You may want to make other stories to tell with your box theater.

The princess in **Sleeping Beauty** was awakened by a kiss.

Wake Up Puppet

Here is what you need:

- round salt carton with pour spout
- print fabric or paper napkin
- rubber band
- pink poster paint and paintbrush
- brown yarn
- masking tape
- pink, white, and red construction paper scraps
- blue marker
- scissors
- white glue

Here is what you do:

1. Cut the bottom out of the salt carton. Cover the entire spout with masking tape. The outside needs to be covered so that the glue will stick to it. The inside edges need to be covered because they can be sharp. Do this carefully.

2. Paint the top of the carton pink for the face.

3. Cut eyes, a nose, and a mouth from construction paper. Color in the center of each eye with the marker. Glue the facial features on, with the eyes on each side and just below the spout.

back of eyelids

glue

4. Cut two eyelids, attached to each other, that are large enough to cover the eyes when set on top of them. Cut yarn eyelashes to glue along the bottom of each lid. Glue the lids to the spout of the salt carton. When you put your hand inside the carton, you should be able to open and shut the eyes by pushing and pulling on the spout.

5. Cut yarn hair to glue around the face of the puppet.

6. Dress the puppet by wrapping the salt carton in a pretty napkin and holding it in place with a rubber band. You can hide the rubber band by folding the napkin down over it.

Find a handsome prince to wake this puppet up with a kiss!

About the Author and Artists

Thirty years as a teacher and director of nursery school programs have given Kathy Ross extensive experience in guiding young children through craft projects. Among the more than forty craft books she has written are *Crafts for All Seasons*, *Kathy Ross Crafts Letter Shapes*, *All New Crafts for Valentine's Day*, *Crafts that Celebrate Black History*, and *Play-Doh™ Fun and Games*. To find out more about Kathy, visit her Web site: www.kathyross.com.

Elaine Garvin designs and illustrates greeting cards and she has illustrated more than twenty children's books over the past ten years. A member of the Society of Children's Book Writers and Illustrators and the Graphic Artists Guild, she lives and works in Massachusetts.

Vicky Enright has illustrated a number of Kathy Ross craft books, and has just completed her first picture book: *Read Anything Good Lately?* by Susan Allen and Jane Lindaman. Vicky lives in Andover, Massachusetts, with two small sons, two huge Labrador retriever dogs, and her husband.